Lambert M. Surhone, Mariam T. Tennoe,
Susan F. Henssonow (Ed.)

DB13W3

AF145835

Lambert M. Surhone, Mariam T. Tennoe,
Susan F. Henssonow (Ed.)

DB13W3

**D-Subminiature, Sun Microsystems, List Of
Display Interfaces**

Betascript Publishing

Imprint

Permission is granted to copy, distribute and/or modify this document under the terms of the GNU Free Documentation License, Version 1.2 or any later version published by the Free Software Foundation; with no Invariant Sections, with the Front-Cover Texts, and with the Back-Cover Texts. A copy of the license is included in the section entitled "GNU Free Documentation License".

All parts of this book are extracted from Wikipedia, the free encyclopedia (www.wikipedia.org).

You can get detailed informations about the authors of this collection of articles at the end of this book. The editors (Ed.) of this book are no authors. They have not modified or extended the original texts.

Pictures published in this book can be under different licences than the GNU Free Documentation License. You can get detailed informations about the authors and licences of pictures at the end of this book.

The content of this book was generated collaboratively by volunteers. Please be advised that nothing found here has necessarily been reviewed by people with the expertise required to provide you with complete, accurate or reliable information. Some information in this book maybe misleading or wrong. The Publisher does not guarantee the validity of the information found here. If you need specific advice (f.e. in fields of medical, legal, financial, or risk management questions) please contact a professional who is licensed or knowledgeable in that area.

Any brand names and product names mentioned in this book are subject to trademark, brand or patent protection and are trademarks or registered trademarks of their respective holders. The use of brand names, product names, common names, trade names, product descriptions etc. even without a particular marking in this works is in no way to be construed to mean that such names may be regarded as unrestricted in respect of trademark and brand protection legislation and could thus be used by anyone.

Cover image: www.ingimage.com
Concerning the licence of the cover image please contact ingimage.

Contact:
VDM Publishing House Ltd.,17 Rue Meldrum, Beau Bassin,1713-01 Mauritius
Email: info@vdm-publishing-house.com
Website: www.vdm-publishing-house.com

Published in 2010
Printed in: U.S.A., U.K., Germany. This book was not produced in Mauritius.

ISBN: 978-613-4-52338-7

Contents

Articles

References

Article Licenses

DB13W3

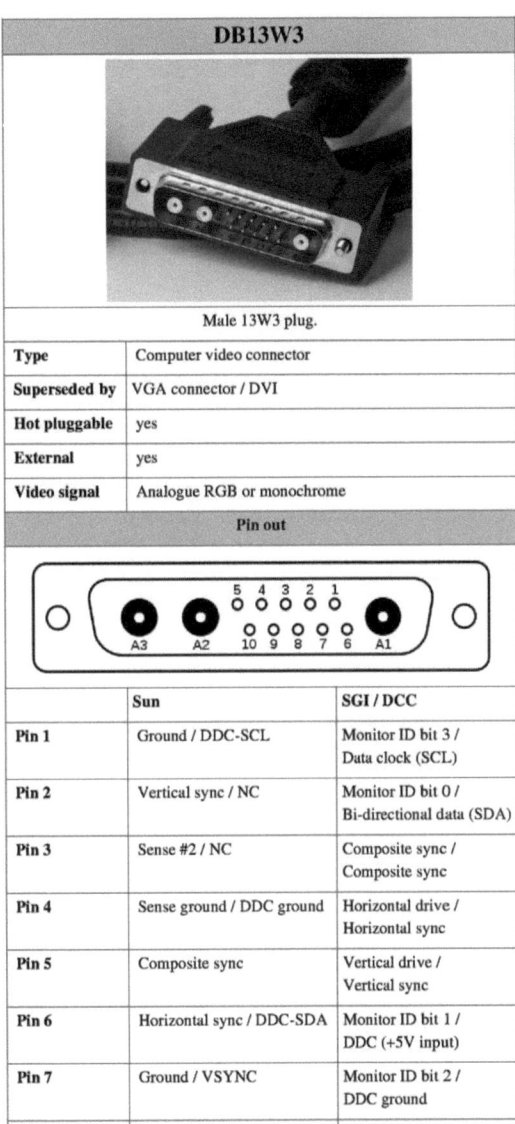

DB13W3	
	Male 13W3 plug.
Type	Computer video connector
Superseded by	VGA connector / DVI
Hot pluggable	yes
External	yes
Video signal	Analogue RGB or monochrome
Pin out	

	Sun	SGI / DCC
Pin 1	Ground / DDC-SCL	Monitor ID bit 3 / Data clock (SCL)
Pin 2	Vertical sync / NC	Monitor ID bit 0 / Bi-directional data (SDA)
Pin 3	Sense #2 / NC	Composite sync / Composite sync
Pin 4	Sense ground / DDC ground	Horizontal drive / Horizontal sync
Pin 5	Composite sync	Vertical drive / Vertical sync
Pin 6	Horizontal sync / DDC-SDA	Monitor ID bit 1 / DDC (+5V input)
Pin 7	Ground / VSYNC	Monitor ID bit 2 / DDC ground
Pin 8	Sense #1 / NC	Digital ground / Ground
Pin 9	Sense #0 /NC	Digital ground / Ground

Pin 10	Composite ground	Sync ground / Ground
A1	Red	Red
A2	Green (Gray for monochrome)	Green (Gray for monochrome)
A3	Blue	Blue

DB13W3 (also known simply as **13W3**) is a particular style of D-subminiature connector commonly used as an analog video interface connector that was used primarily on Sun Microsystems, Silicon Graphics and IBM RISC workstations, as well as some displays from Apple Computer, NeXT Computer and Intergraph Corporation . The 13W3 connector is no longer used with modern displays, which have generally moved on to VGA or DVI connectors. The DB13W3 connector is also used by some 3Com SuperStack Ethernet switches to carry DC power.

The connector contains 10 standard signal pins and 3 larger positions that can be fitted with either special pins with two concentric contacts for coaxial cable or with special high current pins. When used for video signals on the computer side, the pins are female but the coaxial connectors in the large positions are male. The coaxial connectors carry the video signal split into red, green/gray, and blue; the standard signal pins carry four grounds, three "sense" pins used to communicate with the monitor, vertical sync, horizontal sync, and a composite sync signal.

The 13W3 connector can be converted into a standard VGA connector using cables and adapters that are commonly available. This allows modern multisync monitors, which are common on today's computers, to be used with these workstations as long as they are sync-on-green compatible. Likewise, as many newer Sun monitors support multisync, similar cables can be used to connect them to modern computers.

Even though 13W3 is a standard connector the sync signals are maintained on different pins based on the display and system. Sun Microsystems, Intergraph, IBM RISC and SGI have a different set of pins used for the monitor sense IDs and the sync signals. Sun even has two different pinnings: the "classic" one, and one with DDC that was used at least on the UPA graphics adapters (Creator 3D, Expert 3D) and for the corresponding monitors (GD5410, GD5510). This can make matching the correct cable to the monitor virtually impossible. Many monitors with 13W3 connectors do not support separate sync as supplied on most PC systems. Other converters exist to allow connecting newer monitors with VGA connectors to the older systems and workstations. The most popular of these is a cable that allows you to set the sync signals with a series of DIP switches built into the cables.

See also

- List of display interfaces

External links

- 13w3 connector applications and pinouts [1]
- Example of an Apple Inc. card which uses a 13w3 connector [2]

References

[1] http://pinouts.ru/connector/13_pin_13W3_female_connector.shtml
[2] http://www.forcedperfect.net/hardware/cards/workstationportraitcard/

D-subminiature

The **D-subminiature** or **D-sub** is a common type of electrical connector used particularly in computers. At the time of introduction they were some of the smaller connectors used on computer systems.

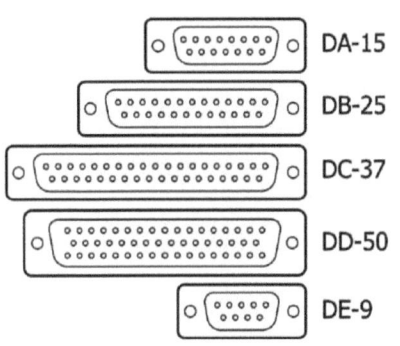

DA, DB, DC, DD, and DE sized connectors

Description and nomenclature

A D-sub contains two or more parallel rows of pins or sockets usually surrounded by a D-shaped metal shield that provides mechanical support, some screening against electromagnetic interference, and ensures correct orientation. The part containing pin contacts is called the *male connector* or *plug*, while that containing socket contacts is called the *female connector* or *socket*. The socket's shield fits tightly inside the plug's shield. The shields are connected to the overall screens of the cables (when screened cables are used). This creates an electrically continuous screen covering the whole cable and connector system.

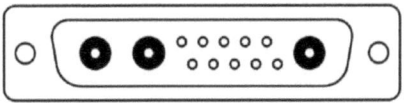

The DB13W3 Connector with 3 coaxial connections and ten ordinary pins

D-subminiature connectors were invented by ITT Cannon, part of ITT Corporation, in 1952.[1] Cannon's part-numbering system uses a D as the prefix for the whole series, followed by a letter denoting the shell size (A=15 pin, B=25 pin, C=37 pin, D=50 pin, E=9 pin), followed by the actual number of pins, followed by the gender (P=plug, S=socket).[2] For example, DB25 denotes a D-sub with a 25 position shell size and a 25 position contact configuration. The contacts in these connectors are spaced approximately 0.109 inches (2.77 mm) apart with the rows spaced 0.112 inches

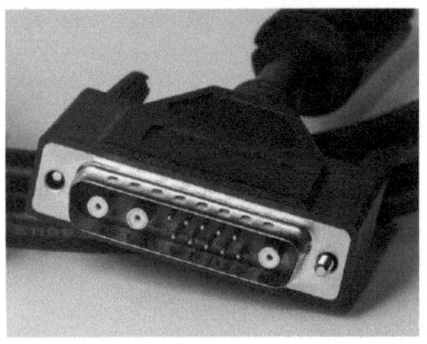

Male 13W3 Plug

(2.84 mm) apart.[3] (To be precise, the horizontal contact spacing is 326/3000 = 108⅔/1000 = 0.108⅔ inch per row, with the second row offset by half that amount.)

Cannon also produced "hybrid" D-subs with larger positions in place of some of the normal pin positions that could be used for either high-current, high-voltage, or co-axial inserts. The DB13W3 variant was commonly used for high-performance video connections; this variant provided 10 regular (#20) pins plus three coaxial contacts for the red, green, and blue video signals. Hybrid D-subs are currently being manufactured in a broad range of configurations by other companies, including Amphenol, Conec,

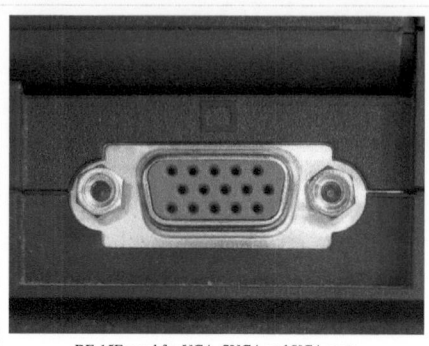

DE-15F, used for VGA, SVGA and XGA ports

Teledyne Reynolds, Assmann Electronics, Norcomp, Cinch, 3M, and Tyco. Variations include current ratings up to 40A, operating voltages as high as 13,500V, and waterproof variants that are certified to IP67 standards.

In the photograph below, the connector on the left is a 9-pin male (DE-9M) connector plug, and the one on the right is a 25-pin female (DB-25F) socket. The hexagonal pillars at either end of each connector have a threaded stud (not visible) that passes through flanges on the connector, fastening it to the metal panel. They also have a threaded hole that receives the jackscrews on the cable shell, to hold the plug and socket together.

Because PCs first used DB25 connectors for their serial and parallel ports, when the PC serial port began to use 9-pin connectors, they were often called "DB9" instead of DE9, due to the lack of understanding that the "B" represented a shell size. It is now common to see DE9 connectors sold as "DB9" connectors. *DB-9* is nearly always intended to be a 9 pin connector with an *E* size shell.

The non-standard 23-pin D-sub connectors for external floppy drives and video output on most of the Amiga computers are usually referred to as DB23, even though their shell size is two pins smaller than ordinary DB sockets.

There are now D-sub connectors which have the original shell sizes, but more pins, and the names follow the same pattern. For example, the DE15, usually found in VGA cables, has 15 pins, in three rows, in an E size shell. The pins are spaced 0.090 inch horizontally and 0.078 inch vertically.[3]) The full list of connectors with this pin spacing is: DE15, DA26, DB44, DC62, and DD78. Alternatively, following the same confusion mentioned above in which all D-sub connectors are called "DB", these connectors are often called DB15HD, DB26HD, DB44HD, DB62HD, and DB78HD, where the "HD" stands for "high density". They all have 3 rows of pins, except the DD78, which has 4.

A series of D-sub connectors with even denser pins is called "double density", and consists of DE19, DA31, DB52, DC79, and DD100. They have 4 rows of pins.

There is yet another similar family of connectors that is easy to confuse with the D-sub family, but is not part of it. These connectors have names like "HD50" and "HD68", and have a D-shaped shell but the shell is about half the width of a DB25. They are common in SCSI attachments.

The suffixes M and F (male and female) are sometimes used instead of the original P and S (plug and socket).

The original D-subminiature connectors are now defined by an international standard, DIN 41652. The United States military also specifies D-subminiature connectors using the MIL-DTL-24308 standard.[3]

Typical applications

Communications ports

The widest application of D-subs is for RS-232 serial communications, though the standard did not make this connector mandatory. RS-232 devices originally used the DB25 25-pin D-sub, but for many applications the less common signals were omitted, allowing a DE9 9-pin D-sub to be used. The standard indicates a male connector for terminal equipment and a female connector for modems, but many variations exist. IBM PC compatible computers tend to have male connectors at the device, while modems have female connectors. Early Apple Macintosh models used DE9 connectors for RS-422 serial interfaces (which can operate as RS-232). Later Macintosh models used 8 pin miniature DIN connectors instead.

D-sub connectors.
Left: DE9M   Right: DB25F.

On PCs, 25-pin and (beginning with the IBM-PC/AT) 9-pin plugs are used for the RS-232 serial ports; and 25-pin sockets are used for the parallel printer ports (instead of the Centronics socket found on the printer itself).

25-pin sockets on Macintosh computers are typically SCSI connectors (again in contrast to the Centronics C50 connector typically found on the peripheral).

Many uninterruptible power supply units have a DE9F connector on them, in order to signal to the attached computer via an RS-232 interface. Often these do not send data serially to the computer but instead use the handshaking control lines to indicate low battery, power failure or other conditions. Such usage is not standardized between manufacturers and may require special cables to be supplied.

Network ports

The RS-422 capability of Macintosh serial ports was used for AppleTalk/LocalTalk networking. (This is also true of Apple IIgs—though it never used D-sub connectors for this.)

DE9 connectors are also used for some token ring and other computer networks. The DA15S was also used for the AUI connectors included on Ethernet cards in the 1980s and 1990s, albeit with a sliding latch to lock the connectors together instead of the usual hex studs with threaded holes. (The sliding latch was intended to be quicker to engage and disengage and to work in places where jack-screws could not be used for reasons of component shape.)

Computer video output

A female 9-pin connector on an IBM compatible personal computer may be a video display output: monochrome, CGA, or EGA. Even though these all use the same connector, the displays cannot all be interchanged and monitors or video interfaces may even be damaged if connected to an incompatible device using the same connector. Later analog video (VGA and later) adapters replaced these connectors by DE15 15-pin high-density sockets, which have three rows of five contacts each in the space that was previously occupied by two rows of contacts, five in the top row and four in the bottom row. Other common names for DE15 connectors are HD15, where HD stands for High Density, and (less accurately) DB15 and DB15HD.

Many Apple Macintosh models (beginning with the Macintosh II) used DA15 sockets for analogue RGB video out. Just prior to this, the Apple IIgs used the same connector for the same purpose, but in a non-compatible way. A digital (and thus also incompatible) RGB adapter for the Apple IIe also used a DA15F. And the Apple IIc used a DA15F for an auxiliary video port which was not RGB, but provided the necessary signals to derive RGB.

Game controller ports

From the late 1970s and all through the '80s, DE9 connectors without the pair of fastening screws (female on the computer or console, male on the controller) were used as game controller connectors in a variety of video game consoles and home computers, quite possibly due to the success of the Atari 2600 game console that used them. Computer systems using them included the Atari 8-bit and ST lines; the Commodore VIC-20, 64, 128, and Amiga; the Amstrad CPC (which employed daisy-chaining when connecting two joysticks, a feature only Amstrad-specific sticks supported); the SEGA Master System and Genesis and the 3D0. The Sinclair ZX Spectrum—which lacked a built in joystick connector of any kind—was commonly used with adapters for DE9 joysticks. While these systems used similar connectors, they were not all electrically compatible. The most common wiring supported one digital (3 positions x 2 axes, 1 button) joystick, or one pair of analog paddles. On many systems a computer mouse or a light pen was also supported through these sockets; however these mice were not usually interchangeable between different systems.

The Apple IIe, IIc, IIc+, IIgs and some Apple II compatibles also used DE9 connectors for joysticks, but they had a male port on the computer and a female on the controller, used analog rather than digital sticks, and the pin-out was completely unlike that used on the aforementioned systems. DE9 connectors were not used for game ports on the Apple Macintosh, Apple III, IBMoid PC systems, or most newer game consoles.

DA15S connectors are used for PC joystick connectors, where each DA15 connector supports two joysticks each with two analog axes and two buttons. In other words, one DA15S "game adapter" connector has 4 analog potentiometer inputs and 4 digital switch inputs. This interface is strictly input-only, though it does provide +5V DC power. Some joysticks with more than two axes and/or more than two buttons use the signals designated for both joysticks. Conversely, Y-adapter cables are available that allow two separate joysticks to be connected to a single DA15 game adapter port; if a joystick connected to one of these Y-adapters has more than two axes or buttons, only the first two of each will work.

The IBM DA15 PC game connector has been modified to add a (usually MPU-401 compatible) MIDI interface, and this is often implemented in the game connectors on third-party sound cards, particularly the Sound Blaster line from Creative Labs. The "standard" straight game adapter connector (introduced by IBM) has three ground pins and four +5V power pins, and the MIDI adaptation replaces one of the grounds and one of the +5V pins, both on the bottom row of pins, with MIDI In and MIDI Out signal pins. (There is no MIDI Thru provided.) Creative Labs introduced this adaptation.

Other

The complete range of D-sub connectors also includes 15-pin DA15s (two rows of 7 and 8); 37-pin DC37s (two rows of 18 and 19); and 50-pin DD50s (two rows of 17 and one of 16), the last two being used in industrial products.

The early Macintosh, and late Apple II computers used an obscure 19 pin D-sub for connecting to external floppy disk drives. And the Commodore Amiga used an equally unusual 23-pin version for both its video output and for connecting an external floppy disk drive.

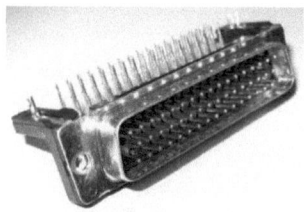

A male PCB-mounting DD50 D-sub connector

TASCAM used DB25 connectors for their multi-track recording audio equipment (TDIF), and Logitek Audio later did the same for its broadcast consoles, though with different pinouts.[4] A few patch panels have been made which have the DB25 connectors on the back with phone jacks (or even TRS jacks) on the front, however these are normally wired for TASCAM, which is more common outside of broadcasting.

In broadcast and professional video, "parallel digital" is a digital video interface that utilizes DB25 connectors, per the SMPTE 274M specification adopted in the late 1990s. The more common SMPTE 259M "serial digital interface" (SDI) utilizes BNC connectors for digital video signal transfer.

A male DE-9 connector.

Types and variants

D-sub connectors exist in at least five types, differentiated by the method used to attach wires to the contacts. These are *solder-cup* or *solder-bucket*, *insulation displacement*, *crimp*, *PCB pins*, and *wire wrap*.

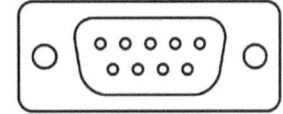

- Solder-bucket contacts have a cavity into which the stripped wire is inserted and hand-soldered (a somewhat tricky process especially to do alone as the wire can easily pop out of the bucket whilst soldering unless held there).
- Insulation displacement contacts (IDC) allow a ribbon cable to be forced onto sharp tines on the back of the contacts; this action pierces the insulation of all the wires simultaneously. This is a very quick means of assembly whether done by hand or automatically but requires use of flat ribbon cable which can be awkward to handle and makes it difficult to make cables with different connections at each end.
- Crimp contacts are assembled by inserting a stripped wire end into a cavity in the rear of the contact, then crushing the cavity using a *crimp tool* causing it to grip the wire tightly at many points. The crimped contact is then inserted into the connector where it locks into place. Individual crimped pins can be removed later with a tool inserted into the rear of the connector. This "rear release" feature is valuable when pins are damaged or modifications must be made to the circuits.
- PCB pins as the name suggests are intended to be soldered directly to a printed circuit board and not to a wire. These connectors are frequently mounted at a right-angle to the PCB allowing a cable to be plugged into the edge of the PCB assembly. Blocks containing multiple stacked D connectors (and sometimes other connectors too) are nearly always seen on ATX (or variants thereof) PC motherboards but aren't generally seen elsewhere.
- Wire wrap connections are made by wrapping solid wire around a square post with a wire wrap tool. This type of connection is usually used in prototyping.

A smaller type of connector derived from the D-subminiature, and about half the linear size, is called the microminiature D, or micro-D, which is a trademark of ITT Cannon. This connector is used in industrial instrumentation products. A few manufacturers make nano-D connectors, which are about half the size again.

Usage

The 25 pin D-sub connector is occasionally used in the recording studio industry for multi-channel analog audio and AES Digital audio.

The D-sub connector family is now in decline for general usage in the computer industry, due to size and cost. For portable devices such as PDAs, MP3 players or mobile phones, the D-sub connector is usually too large to fit. In the laptop computer sector, where weight and size are crucial, many models no longer include D-subs. Even small form factor desktop PCs may find D-sub connectors too large for their value.

Because of the relatively complex shapes and assembly, especially the shaped metal D shield, and screws and nuts for physical securing, D-sub connectors are now quite expensive compared to other, mostly simpler, common connectors. In the retail PC world where margins are very thin, these connectors are a natural target for removal.

The physical design is not friendly to consumer plug-and-play applications. Thin metal pins, especially in higher-density connectors, are easily bent or broken, especially when frequently plugged in "blind" behind equipment. The need to tighten screws for a secure connection is cumbersome. Although ESD and EMI resistant D-sub connectors exist, the fundamental design was never intended to protect from electrostatic discharge or electromagnetic interference or facilitate very high frequency interconnections.

For video purposes, the DE15HD connector is in the process of being replaced by DVI and HDMI connectors. A notable exception to this replacement is on the many analog CRT monitors still in use - the analog version of the DVI connector is similar in price and more complex than the D-sub, so adoption in this field is slow.

For the majority of other consumer applications, D-sub serial and parallel connectors have been replaced by the physically much simpler and cheaper IEEE 1394 (FireWire), SATA, USB or Ethernet connectors.

See also

- Gender of connectors and fasteners
- RS-232 Technical Manual
- Micro ribbon
- Modular connector
- MMJ

References

[1] Are D Subs from all manufactures compatible? (http://www.ittcannon.com/content.aspx?id=56) — reply in the FAQ section of the Cannon company web
[2] *ITT Cannon 90° PCB Selection Guide* (http://docs-europe.origin.electrocomponents.com/webdocs/0027/0900766b80027708.pdf), accessed at RS Components website on 2007-09-10
[3] "List Mil Specs - DSCC" (http://www.dscc.dla.mil/Programs/MilSpec/ListDocs.asp?BasicDoc=MIL-DTL-24308). Dscc.dla.mil. . Retrieved 2010-08-18.
[4] "DTRS - Analog DB25 Pin-out" (http://www.tascam.com/i-913-232-128-1-5061CAA6.pdf) (PDF). . Retrieved 2010-08-18.

External links

- Comprehsive DB25 wiring diagrams: Tascam, Apple, SCSI, etc.. (http://pinouts.ru/connector/25_pin_D-SUB_male_connector.shtml)
- Ishmael Stefanov-Wagner's web page on D-Subminiature Nomenclature (http://research.meei.harvard.edu/EPL/Engineering/d-subminiature.html)
- A list of common computer connectors, including most D-sub (http://pinouts.ru/connector/)
- Devices with DE-9 connectors (http://pinouts.ru/connector/9_pin_D-SUB_female_connector.shtml)
- DE-9 Connector RS-232 Pinout (http://www.db9-pinout.com)

Sun Microsystems

Type	Subsidiary of Oracle Corporation
Industry	Computer systems Computer software
Founded	1982
Founder(s)	Vinod Khosla Andy Bechtolsheim Bill Joy Scott McNealy
Headquarters	Santa Clara, California, USA
Key people	Dorian Daley (President & CEO) Jeffrey Epstein (CFO)[1]
Products	Servers Workstations Storage Services
Revenue	▼ US$11.449 billion (2009)[2]
Operating income	▼ US$2.236 billion (2009)[2]
Net income	▼ US$2.234 billion (2009)[2]
Total assets	▼ US$11.232 billion (2009)[2]
Total equity	▼ US$3.305 billion (2009)[2]
Employees	29,000 (2009)[3]
Parent	Oracle Corporation
Website	http://www.oracle.com/sun

Sun Microsystems, Inc. was a company selling computers, computer components, computer software, and information technology services. Sun was founded on February 24, 1982.[4] The company was headquartered in Santa Clara, California (part of Silicon Valley), on the former west campus of the Agnews Developmental Center.

On January 27, 2010, Sun was acquired by Oracle Corporation for US$7.4 billion, based on an agreement signed on April 20, 2009.[5] Sun Microsystems, Inc. was subsequently renamed **Oracle America, Inc.** [6]

Sun products included computer servers and workstations based on its own SPARC processors as well as AMD's Opteron and Intel's Xeon processors; storage systems; and, a suite of software products including the Solaris operating system, developer tools, Web infrastructure software, and identity management applications. Other technologies of note include the Java platform, MySQL, and NFS. Sun was a proponent of open systems in general and Unix in particular, and a major contributor to open source software.[7] Sun's main manufacturing facilities were located in Hillsboro, Oregon and Linlithgow, Scotland.

History

The initial design for what became Sun's first Unix workstation, the Sun-1, was conceived by Andy Bechtolsheim when he was a graduate student at Stanford University in Palo Alto, California. He originally designed the SUN workstation for the Stanford University Network communications project as a personal CAD workstation. It was designed as a 3M computer: 1 MIPS, 1 Megabyte and 1 Megapixel. It was designed around the Motorola 68000 processor with an advanced

Original Sun Microsystems logo, as used on the nameplate of the Sun-1 workstation

Memory management unit (MMU) to support the Unix operating system with virtual memory support.[8] He built the first ones from spare parts obtained from Stanford's Department of Computer Science and Silicon Valley supply houses.[9]

On February 24, 1982 Vinod Khosla, Andy Bechtolsheim, and Scott McNealy, all Stanford graduate students, founded *Sun Microsystems*. Bill Joy of Berkeley, a primary developer of BSD, joined soon after and is counted as one of the original founders.[10] The Sun name is derived from the initials of the Stanford University Network.[11] [12] Sun was profitable from its first quarter in July 1982.

Sun's initial public offering was in 1986 under the stock symbol *SUNW*, for *Sun Workstations* (later *Sun Worldwide*).[13] [14] The symbol was changed in 2007 to *JAVA*; Sun stated that the brand awareness associated with its Java platform better represented the company's current strategy.[15]

Sun's logo, which features four interleaved copies of the word *sun*, was designed by professor Vaughan Pratt, also of Stanford University. The initial version of the logo was orange and had the sides oriented horizontally and vertically, but it was subsequently redesigned so as to appear to stand on one corner and the color changed to purple.

Revised logo, used until early 1990s

Ingrid Van Den Hoogen (Sun's Senior Vice President of Corporate Marketing) asked Sun's staff from around the world to share some of their favorite anecdotes about their experiences at Sun. A Tribute to Sun Microsystems [16], containing videos, stories, and photographs from 27 years at Sun, was made available on September 2, 2009.

The "Bubble" and its aftermath

During the dot-com bubble, Sun experienced dramatic growth in revenue, profits, share price, and expenses. Some part of this was due to genuine expansion of demand for web-serving cycles, but another part was synthetic, fueled by venture capital-funded startups building out large, expensive Sun-centric server presences in the expectation of high traffic levels that never materialized. The share price in that particular period increased to a level that even the company's

Logo used from 1990s until acquisition by Oracle

executives were hard-pressed to defend. In response to this business growth, Sun expanded aggressively in all areas: head-count, infrastructure, and office space.

The bursting of the bubble in 2001 was the start of a period of poor business performance for Sun.[17] Sales dropped as the growth of online business failed to meet predictions. As online businesses closed and their assets were auctioned off, a large amount of used high-end Sun hardware was available very cheaply. This hurt Sun's business as it relied a great deal on hardware sales.

Multiple quarters of substantial losses and declining revenues have led to repeated rounds of layoffs,[18] [19] [20] executive departures, and expense-reduction efforts. In December 2001 the share price dropped to the 1998 pre-bubble level of about one hundred dollars or so and then kept going, a rapid fall even by the standards of the high-tech sector at that time. The stock dipped below 10 dollars a year later, one-tenth of its 1990 value, then quickly bounced back to 20. In mid-2004, Sun ceased manufacturing operations at their Newark, California facility and consolidated all of the company's US-based manufacturing operations to their Hillsboro, Oregon facility, as part of continued cost-reduction efforts.[21] In 2006 Sun closed the Newark campus completely and moved 2,300 staff to its other campuses in the area.[22]

Many companies (like E-Trade and Google) chose to build Web applications based on large numbers of the less expensive PC-class x86-architecture servers running Linux, rather than a smaller number of high-end Sun servers. They reported benefits including substantially lower expenses (both acquisition and maintenance) and greater flexibility based on the use of open-source software. Sun responded to this in several ways, including introducing its own lines of x86-based servers to compete directly in that market, re-launching development of Solaris on the x86 platform and releasing the open-source OpenSolaris to drive interest in using Solaris, and coming out with lower cost horizontally-scaled SPARC systems.

Post-crash focus

In 2004, Sun canceled two major processor projects which emphasized high instruction level parallelism and operating frequency. Instead, the company chose to concentrate on processors optimized for multi-threading and multiprocessing, such as the UltraSPARC T1 processor (codenamed "Niagara"). The company also announced a collaboration with Fujitsu to use the Japanese company's processor chips in mid-range and high-end Sun servers. These servers were announced on April 17, 2007 as the M-Series, part of the SPARC Enterprise series.

Aerial photograph of the Sun headquarters campus in Santa Clara, California.

In February 2005, Sun announced the Sun Grid, a grid computing deployment on which it offers utility computing services priced at US$1 per CPU/hour for processing and per GB/month for storage. This offering builds upon an existing 3,000-CPU server farm used for internal R&D for over 10 years, which Sun markets as being able to achieve 97% utilization. In August 2005, the first commercial use of this grid was announced for financial risk simulations which was later launched as its first Software as a Service product.[23]

Buildings 21 and 22 at Sun's headquarters campus in Santa Clara

In January 2005, Sun reported a net profit of $19 million for fiscal 2005 second quarter, for the first time in three years. This was followed by net loss of $9 million on GAAP basis for the third quarter 2005, as reported on April 14, 2005. In January 2007, Sun reported a net GAAP profit of $126 million on revenue of $3.337 billion for its fiscal second quarter. Shortly following that news, it was announced that Kohlberg Kravis Roberts (KKR) would invest $700 million in the company.[24]

In recent years Sun's engineering work has become international, with substantial groups in Bangalore, Beijing, Dublin, Grenoble, Hamburg, Prague, St. Petersburg, Tel Aviv, Tokyo, and Trondheim.[25]

In 2007–2008, Sun posted revenue of $13.8 billion and had $2 billion in cash. First-quarter 2008 losses were $1.68 billion; revenue fell 7% to $2.99 billion. Sun's stock lost 80% of its value November 2007 to November 2008, reducing the company's market value to $3 billion. With falling sales to large corporate clients, Sun announced plans to lay off 5,000 to 6,000 workers, or 15-18% of its work force. It expected to save $700 million to $800 million a year as a result of the moves, while also taking up to $600 million in charges.[26]

Sun in Markham, Ontario, Canada

Sun acquisitions

This list is incomplete.

Sun server racks at Seneca College (York Campus)

- 1987 - Trancept Systems, a high performance graphics hardware company[27]
- 1987 - Centram Systems West, maker of networking software for PCs, Macs and Sun systems
- 1988 - Folio, Inc., developer of intelligent font scaling technology and the F3 font format[28]
- 1991 - INTERACTIVE Systems Corporation's Intel/Unix OS division, from Eastman Kodak Company
- 1992 - Praxsys Technologies, Inc., developers of the Windows emulation technology that eventually became Wabi[29]

- 1994 - Thinking Machines Corporation hardware division
- 1996 - Lighthouse Design, Ltd.[30]
- 1996 - Cray Business Systems Division, from Silicon Graphics[31]
- 1996 - Integrated Micro Products, specializing in fault tolerant servers
- 1996 - Thinking Machines Corporation software division
- February 1997 - LongView Technologies, LLC[32]
- August 1997 - Diba, a technology supplier for the Information Appliance industry[33]
- September 1997 - Chorus Systems, creators of ChorusOS[34]
- November 1997 - Encore Computer Corporation's storage business[35]
- 1998 - RedCape Software
- 1998 - i-Planet, a small software company that produced the "Pony Espresso" mobile email client—most notable product of this acquisition was the later use of its name (sans hyphen) for the Sun-Netscape software alliance
- July 1998 - NetDynamics[36] - developers of the NetDynamics Application Server[37]
- 1999 - German software company StarDivision and with it StarOffice, which was later released as open source under the name OpenOffice.org
- 1999 - MAXSTRAT Corporation, a network storage company located in Milpitas, CA specializing in Fibre Channel storage servers.
- 1999 - Forte, an enterprise software company specializing in integration solutions and developer of the Forte 4GL and TeamWare.
- 1999 - NetBeans, a newly formed business producing a modular IDE written in Java, based on a student project at Charles University in Prague.

- March 2000 - Innosoft International, Inc. a software company specializing in highly scalable MTAs (PMDF) and Directory Services.
- July 2000 - Gridware, a software company whose products managed the distribution of large computing jobs across multiple computers[38]
- September 2000 - Cobalt Networks, an Internet appliance manufacturer[39]
- December 2000 - HighGround, with a suite of Web-based management solutions support wide range of storage technologies and applications[40]
- 2001 - LSC, Inc., an Eagan, Minnesota company that developed Storage and Archive Management File System(SAM-FS) and Quick File System QFS high performance file systems for backup and archive
- March 2002 - Clustra Systems[41]
- June 2002 - Afara Websystems, a company that develops next-generation SPARC processor-based technology[42]
- September 2002 - Pirus Networks, specializing in intelligent storage services[43]
- November 2002 - Terraspring, a pioneer in infrastructure automation software[44]
- June 2003 - Pixo, adds to the capabilities of the Sun Content Delivery Server[45]
- August 2003 - CenterRun, Inc.[46]
- December 2003 - Waveset Technologies, an identity management solutions company[47]
- January 2004 - Nauticus Networks[48]
- February 2004 - Kealia, a startup founded by original Sun founder Andy Bechtolsheim, which had been focusing on high-performance AMD-based 64-bit servers[49]
- January 2005 - SevenSpace, a multi-platform managed services provider[50]
- May 2005 - Tarantella, Inc. (formerly known as Santa Cruz Operation (SCO)), for $25,000,000[51]
- June 2005 - SeeBeyond, a Service-Oriented Architecture (SOA) software company for $387m[52]
- June 2005 - Procom Technology, Inc.'s NAS IP Assets[53]
- August 2005 - StorageTek[54]
- February 2006 - Aduva, producer of software for Solaris and Linux patch management[55]
- October 2006 - Neogent[56]
- April 2007 - SavaJe, developer of the SavaJe OS, a Java OS for mobile phones
- September 2007 - Cluster File Systems, Inc.[57]
- November 2007 - Vaau, provider of Enterprise Role Management and identity compliance solutions[58]
- February 2008 - MySQL AB, the company offering the popular open source database MySQL[59]
- February 2008 - Innotek GmbH, developer of the VirtualBox virtualization product[60] [61]
- April 2008 - Montalvo Systems, failed x86 microprocessor startup acquired before first silicon
- January 2009 - Q-layer, a software company with cloud computing solutions[62]

Major stockholders

As of May 11, 2009, the following shareholders held over 100,000 common shares of Sun:[63] and at $9.40 per share offered by Oracle they received the amounts indicated when the acquisition closed.

Major Investors in Sun

Investor	Common Shares	Value at Merger
Barclays Global Investors	37,606,402	$353,500,180
Scott G. McNealy	14,566,433	$136,924,470
Kenneth M. Oshman	584,985	$5,498,860
Jonathan I. Schwartz	536,109	$5,039,425
James L. Barksdale	231,785	$2,178,780
Michael E. Lehman	106,684	$1,002,830

Hardware

For the first decade of Sun's history, the company was predominantly a vendor of technical workstations, competing successfully as a low-cost vendor during the Workstation Wars of the 1980s. It now has shifted its hardware product line to emphasize servers and storage. High-level telecom control systems such as NMAS and OSS service predominantly use Sun equipment. This use is due mainly to the company basing its products around a mature and very stable version of the Unix operating system and the support service that Sun provides.

Motorola-based systems

Sun originally used the Motorola 68k CPU family for the Sun-1 through Sun-3 computer series. The Sun-1 employed a 68000 CPU, the Sun-2 series, a 68010. The Sun-3 series was based on the 68020, with the later Sun-3x variant using the 68030.

SPARC-based systems

In 1987, the company began using *SPARC*, a processor architecture of its own design, in its computer systems, starting with the Sun-4 line. SPARC was initially a 32-bit architecture until the introduction of the SPARC V9 architecture in 1995, which added 64-bit extensions.

Sun has developed several generations of SPARC-based computer systems, including the SPARCstation, Ultra and Sun Blade series of workstations, and the SPARCserver, Netra, Enterprise and Sun Fire line of servers.

In the early 1990s the company began to extend its product line to include large-scale symmetric multiprocessing servers, starting with the four-processor SPARCserver 600MP. This was followed by the 8-processor SPARCserver 1000 and 20-processor SPARCcenter 2000, which were based on work done in conjunction with Xerox PARC. In the late 1990s this transformation was accelerated by the acquisition of

SPARCstation 1+

Cray Business Systems Division from Silicon Graphics.[31] Their 32-bit, 64-processor Cray Superserver 6400, related to the SPARCcenter, led to the 64-bit Sun Enterprise 10000 high-end server (otherwise known as *Starfire*). In 2006, Sun has also ventured into the *blade server* (high density rack-mounted systems) market with the Sun Blade (distinct from the Sun Blade workstation).

In November 2005 Sun launched the UltraSPARC T1, notable for its ability to concurrently run 32 threads of execution on 8 processor cores. Its intent was to drive more efficient use of CPU resources, which is of particular importance in data centers, where there is an increasing need to reduce power and air conditioning demands, much of which comes from the heat generated by CPUs. The T1 was followed by the UltraSPARC T2, which extended the number of threads per core from 4 to 8, and T2 Plus, which added the ability to have multiple T2 processors in one system. Sun has open sourced the design specifications of both the T1 and T2 processors via the OpenSPARC project.

In April 2007, Sun released the SPARC Enterprise server products, jointly designed by Sun and Fujitsu and based on Fujitsu SPARC64 VI and later processors. The *M-class* SPARC Enterprise systems include high-end reliability and availability features.

x86-based systems

In the late 1980s, Sun also marketed an Intel 80386-based machine, the Sun386i; this was designed to be a hybrid system, running SunOS but at the same time supporting DOS applications. This only remained on the market for a brief time. A follow-up "486i" upgrade was announced but only a few prototype units were ever manufactured.

Sun's brief first foray into x86 systems ended in the early 1990s, as it decided to concentrate on SPARC and retire the last Motorola systems and 386i products, a move dubbed by McNealy as "all the wood behind one arrowhead". Even so, Sun kept its hand in the x86 world, as a release of Solaris for PC compatibles began shipping in 1993.

In 1997 Sun acquired Diba, Inc., followed later by the acquisition of Cobalt Networks in 2000, with the aim of building *network appliances* (single function computers meant for consumers). Sun also marketed a *network computer* (a term popularized and eventually trademarked by Oracle); the JavaStation was a diskless system designed to run Java applications.

Although none of these business initiatives were particularly successful, the Cobalt purchase gave Sun a toehold for its return to the x86 hardware market. In 2002, Sun introduced its first general purpose x86 system, the LX50, based in part on previous Cobalt system expertise. This was also Sun's first system announced to support Linux as well as Solaris.

In 2003, Sun announced a strategic alliance with AMD to produce x86/x64 servers based on AMD's Opteron processor; this was followed shortly by Sun's acquisition of Kealia, a startup founded by original Sun founder Andy Bechtolsheim, which had been focusing on high-performance AMD-based servers.

The following year, Sun launched the Opteron-based Sun Fire V20z and V40z servers, and the Java Workstation W1100z and W2100z workstations.

On September 12, 2005, Sun unveiled a new range of Opteron-based servers: the Sun Fire X2100, X4100 and X4200 servers.[64] These were designed from scratch by the team led by Bechtolsheim to address heat and power consumption issues commonly faced in data centers. In July 2006, the Sun Fire X4500 and X4600 systems were introduced, extending what is now a line of x64 systems that support not only Solaris, but also Linux and Microsoft Windows.

On January 22, 2007, Sun announced a broad strategic alliance with Intel.[65] Intel now endorses Solaris as a mainstream operating system and as its mission critical UNIX OS for its Xeon processor-based systems, and also contributes engineering resources to OpenSolaris.[66] Sun began using the Intel Xeon processor in its x64 server line, starting with the Sun Blade X6250 server module introduced in June 2007.

On May 5, 2008, AMD announced that its Operating System Research Center (OSRC) expanded its focus to include optimization to Sun's OpenSolaris and xVM virtualization products for AMD based processors.[67]

Software

Although Sun was initially known as a hardware company, its software history began with its founding in 1982; co-founder Bill Joy was one of the leading Unix developers of the time, having already contributed the vi editor, the C shell, and significant work on the TCP/IP stack to the BSD Unix OS. Since then, Sun has developed and acquired other software, and become widely known for the Java programming language.

Sun is known for community-based and open-source licensing of its major technologies, and for its support of its products with other open source technologies. Sun offers GNOME-based desktop software called Java Desktop System (originally code-named "Madhatter"), first distributed as a Linux implementation but now offered as part of the Solaris operating system. It supports its Java Enterprise System (a middleware stack) on Linux. It has released the source code for Solaris under the open-source Common Development and Distribution License, via the OpenSolaris community. Sun's positioning includes a commitment to indemnify users of some software from intellectual property disputes concerning that software. It offers support services on a variety of pricing bases, including per-employee and per-socket.

A report prepared for the EU by UNU-MERIT stated that Sun is the largest corporate contributor to open source movements in the world.[68] According to this report, Sun's open source contributions exceed the combined total of the next five largest commercial contributors.

Operating systems

Sun is most well known for its Unix systems, which have a reputation for system stability and a consistent design philosophy.

Sun's first workstation shipped with UniSoft V7 Unix. Later in 1982 Sun began providing SunOS, a customized 4.1BSD Unix, as the operating system for its workstations.

In the late 1980s, AT&T tapped Sun to help them develop the next release of their branded UNIX, and in 1988 announced they would purchase up to a 20% stake in Sun.[69] UNIX System V Release 4 (SVR4) was jointly developed by AT&T and Sun; this partnership triggered concern among Sun's competitors, many of whom banded together to form the Open Software Foundation (OSF). By the mid-1990s, the ensuing Unix wars had largely subsided, AT&T had sold off their Unix interests, and the relationship between the two companies was significantly reduced.

Sun used SVR4 as the foundation for Solaris 2, which became the successor to SunOS.

From 1992 Sun also sold INTERACTIVE UNIX, an operating system it acquired when it bought INTERACTIVE Systems Corporation from Eastman Kodak Company. This was a popular UNIX variant for the PC platform and a major competitor to market leader SCO UNIX. Sun's focus on INTERACTIVE UNIX diminished in favor of Solaris on both SPARC and x86 systems; it was dropped as a product in 2001.

In the past, Sun has offered a separate variant of Solaris called Trusted Solaris, which included augmented security features such as multilevel security and a least privilege access model. Solaris 10 included many of the same capabilities as Trusted Solaris when it was released in 2005; the Solaris 10 11/06 update included Solaris Trusted Extensions, which give it the remaining capabilities needed to make it the functional successor to Trusted Solaris.

Following several years of difficult competition and loss of server market share to competitors' Linux-based systems, Sun began to include Linux as part of its strategy in 2002. Sun supports both Red Hat Enterprise Linux and SUSE Linux Enterprise Server on its x64 systems; companies such as Canonical Ltd., Wind River Systems and MontaVista also support their versions of Linux on Sun's SPARC-based systems.

In 2004, Sun surprised the industry when, after having cultivated a reputation as one of Microsoft's most vocal antagonists, it entered into a joint relationship with them, resolving various legal entanglements between the two companies and receiving US$1.95 billion in settlement payments from them.[70] Sun now supports Microsoft Windows on its x64 systems, and has announced other collaborative agreements with Microsoft, including plans to support each others' virtualization environments.[71]

Java platform

The Java platform was developed at Sun in the early 1990s with the objective of allowing programs to function regardless of the device they were used on, sparking the slogan "Write once, run anywhere" (WORA). While this objective has not been entirely achieved (prompting the riposte "Write once, debug everywhere"), Java is regarded as being largely hardware- and operating system-independent.

Java was initially promoted as a platform for client-side *applets* running inside web browsers. Early examples of Java applications were the HotJava web browser and the HotJava Views suite. However, since then Java has been more successful on the server side of the Internet.

The platform consists of three major parts, the Java programming language, the Java Virtual Machine (JVM), and several Java Application Programming Interfaces (APIs). The design of the Java platform is controlled by the vendor and user community through the Java Community Process (JCP).

Java is an object-oriented programming language. Since its introduction in late 1995, it has become one of the world's most popular programming languages.[72]

In order to allow programs written in the Java language to be run on virtually any device, Java programs are compiled to byte code, which can be executed by any JVM, regardless of the environment.

The Java APIs provide an extensive set of library routines. These APIs have evolved into the *Standard Edition* (Java SE), which provides basic infrastructure and GUI functionality; the *Enterprise Edition* (Java EE), aimed at large software companies implementing enterprise-class application servers; and the *Micro Edition* (Java ME), used to build software for devices with limited resources, such as mobile devices.

On November 13, 2006, Sun announced that it would be licensing its Java implementation under the GNU General Public License;it released its Java compiler and JVM at that time.[73]

In February 2009 Sun entered a battle with Microsoft and Adobe Systems, which are promoting rival platforms to build software applications for the Internet.[74] JavaFX is a development platform for music, video and other applications that builds on the Java programming language.[74]

Office suite

In 1999, Sun acquired the German software company StarDivision and with it StarOffice, which it released as the office suite OpenOffice.org under both GNU LGPL and the SISSL (Sun Industry Standards Source License). OpenOffice.org supports Microsoft Office file formats (though not perfectly), is available on many platforms (primarily Linux, Microsoft Windows, Mac OS X, and Solaris) and is widely used in the open source community.

The current StarOffice product is a closed-source product based on OpenOffice.org. The principal differences between StarOffice and OpenOffice.org are that StarOffice is supported by Sun, is available as either a single-user retail box kit or as per-user blocks of licensing for the enterprise, and includes a wider range of fonts and document templates and a commercial quality spellchecker.[75] StarOffice also contains commercially licensed functions and add-ons; in OpenOffice.org these are either replaced by open-source or free variants, or are not present at all. Both packages have native support for the OpenDocument format.

Virtualization and datacenter automation software

In 2007, Sun announced the Sun xVM virtualization and datacenter automation product suite for commodity hardware. Sun also acquired VirtualBox in 2008. Earlier virtualization technologies from Sun like *Dynamic System Domains* and *Dynamic Reconfiguration* were specifically designed for high-end SPARC servers, and Logical Domains only supports the UltraSPARC T1/T2/T2 Plus server platforms. Sun also has the *Sun Ops Center* provisioning software for datacenter automation.

On the client side, Sun offers virtual desktop solutions. Complete desktop environments and applications can be hosted in the datacenter, with users accessing these

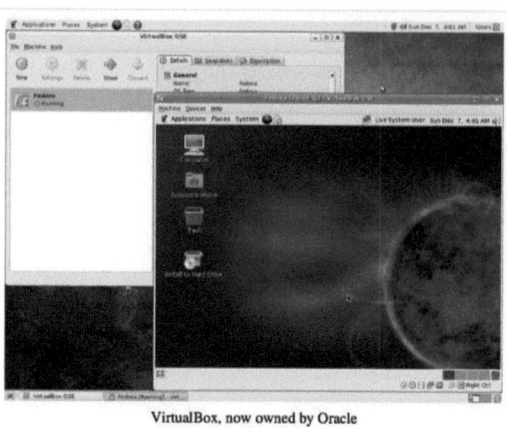

VirtualBox, now owned by Oracle

environments from a wide range of client devices, including Microsoft Windows PCs, Sun Ray virtual display clients, Apple Macintoshes, PDAs or any combination of supported devices. A variety of networks are supported, from LAN to WAN or the public Internet. A virtual desktop solution can be provided through Sun Ray Server Software, Sun Secure Global Desktop and Sun Virtual Desktop Infrastructure.

Database management systems

Sun acquired MySQL AB, the developer of the MySQL database in 2008 for US$ 1 billion.[76] CEO Jonathan Schwartz mentioned in his blog that optimizing the performance of MySQL is one of the priorities of the acquisition.[77] In February 2008, Sun began to publish results of the MySQL performance optimization work.[78] Sun is also a contributor to the PostgreSQL project. On the Java platform, Sun contributes to, ships, and offers support for Java DB.

Other software

Sun offers a range of other software products for software development and infrastructure services. Many of these products were developed in house; others have come from a series of acquisitions, including Tarantella, Waveset Technologies,[47] SeeBeyond, and Vaau. Sun also acquired many of the Netscape non-browser software products as part a deal involving Netscape's merger with AOL.[79] These software products were initially offered under the *iPlanet* brand; once the Sun-Netscape alliance ended, they were re-branded as *Sun ONE* (Sun Open Network Environment), and more recently as the *Sun Java System*.

Today, Sun's middleware stack is branded as the *Java Enterprise System* (or JES), and fulfills web and application serving, as well as communication, calendaring, directory, identity management and SOA/business integration roles. Sun's Open ESB and other software suites are available for download and use free of charge on systems running Solaris, Red Hat Enterprise Linux, HP-UX, and Windows, with support available optionally.

Sun has developed data center management software products, which include the *Solaris Cluster* high availability software, and a grid management package called *Sun Grid Engine* and firewall software such as SunScreen.

For the Network Equipment Providers and the telecommunications world, Sun developed the carrier-grade Netra High-Availability Suite.

Sun also produces a suite of compilers and development tools under the *Sun Studio* brand, for building and developing Solaris and Linux applications.

Sun has recently entered the Software as a Service (SaaS) market with zembly, a social cloud-based computing platform and Project Kenai, an open-source project hosting service.

Storage

Sun has long sold its own storage systems to complement its system offerings; it has also made several storage-related acquisitions. On June 2, 2005, Sun announced it would purchase Storage Technology Corporation (StorageTek) for US$4.1 billion in cash, or $37.00 per share, a deal completed in August 2005.

In 2006, Sun introduced the Sun StorageTek 5800 System, the world's first application-aware programmable storage solution. In 2008, Sun contributed the source code of the StorageTek 5800 System under the BSD license.[80]

Sun announced the Sun Open Storage platform in 2008. Built with open and open source technologies, Sun hopes to remove vendor lock-in in the storage market.

In late 2008 Sun announced the *Sun Storage 7000 Unified Storage Systems* (codenamed Amber Road). Transparent placement of data in the systems' solid-state drives (SSD) and conventional hard drives is managed by ZFS in a way to take advantage of the speed of SSDs and the economy of conventional hard disks.[81]

Other well-known storage products include Sun Fire X4500 storage server and SAM-QFS filesystem and storage management software.

HPC solutions

With Sun Constellation System, Sun is increasing its focus in High-Performance Computing (HPC). Even before the introduction of the Sun Constellation System in 2007, Sun's products were already in use in many of the TOP500 systems and supercomputing centers:

- Lustre - used by 7 of the top 10 supercomputers in 2008, as well as other industries that need scalable and high-performance storage: 6 major oil companies (including BP, Shell, and ExxonMobil), chip-design (including Synopsys and Sony), and the movie-industry (including Harry Potter and Spider-Man).[82]
- Sun Fire X4500 - used by high energy physics supercomputers to run dCache
- Sun Grid Engine - a popular workload scheduler for clusters and compute farms
- Sun Visualization System - allows users of the TeraGrid to remotely access the 3D rendering capabilities of the *Maverick* system at the University of Texas at Austin
- Sun Modular Datacenter (Project Blackbox) - two Sun MD S20 units are used by the Stanford Linear Accelerator Center

The *Sun HPC ClusterTools* product is a set of MPI libraries and tools for running parallel jobs on Solaris HPC clusters. Beginning with version 7.0, Sun switched from its own implementation of MPI to Open MPI, and has started donating engineering resources to the Open MPI project.

Sun is a participant in the OpenMP language committee. Sun Studio compilers and tools natively implement the OpenMP specification for shared memory parallelization.

In 2006, Sun built the *TSUBAME supercomputer*, which was until June 2008 the fastest supercomputer in Asia. Sun built *Ranger* at the Texas Advanced Computing Center (TACC) in 2007. Ranger has a peak performance of over 500 TFLOPS, and is currently the 6th most powerful supercomputer on the TOP500 list (November 2008).

Sun also has an OpenSolaris distribution that is optimized for HPC workloads. The distribution integrates many of Sun's HPC products and other commonly used 3rd-party solutions.[83]

Staff

Notable current and former Sun employees include John Gilmore, Whitfield Diffie, Radia Perlman, Marc Tremblay, and Ned Freed. Sun was an early advocate of Unix-based networked computing, promoting TCP/IP and especially NFS, as reflected in the company's motto "The Network Is The Computer", coined by John Gage. James Gosling led the team which developed the Java programming language. Most recently, Jon Bosak led the creation of the XML specification at W3C.

Many Sun staff published articles on the company's blog site.[84] Staff were encouraged to use the site to blog on any aspect of their work or personal life, with few restrictions placed on staff, other than commercially confidential material. Former CEO Jonathan I. Schwartz was noted as one of the few CEOs of large companies to regularly blog; his postings were frequently quoted and analyzed in the press.[85] [86] [87]

See also

- Callan Data Systems
- Global Education Learning Community
- Interactive Systems Corporation
- Liberty Alliance
- List of computer system manufacturers
- NetBeans
- Open Source University Meetup
- Sun Certified Professional
- Sun Modular Datacenter

References

[1]   "SEC Filing" (http://sec.gov/Archives/edgar/data/709519/000119312510017049/d8k.htm). SEC. . Retrieved 2010-02-01.

[2]   "Financial Tables" (http://www.google.com/finance?fstype=ii&cid=543040). *Sun Microsystems Investor Relations*. . Retrieved 2010-02-18.

[3]   "Company Info" (http://sun.com/aboutsun/company/). *Sun employee database*. . Retrieved 2010-02-18.

[4]   "The Glamor in Mass Transit" (http://blogs.sun.com/jonathan/entry/brutal_efficiency_virtualization_by_another). Sun Microsystems, Inc.. 24 February 2007. . Retrieved 2007-02-25.

[5]   "Oracle Completes Acquisition of Sun" (http://finance.yahoo.com/news/Oracle-Completes-Acquisition-iw-2658323391.html?x=0&. v=1). Yahoo. 27 January 2010. . Retrieved 27 January 2010.

[6]   "Form 8-K/A for ORACLE CORP" (http://biz.yahoo.com/e/100407/orcl8-k_a.html). *Yahoo! Finance*. Oracle Corporation. 7 April 2010. . Retrieved 10 September 2010.

[7]   "Sun begins releasing Java under the GPL" (http://www.fsf.org/news/fsf-welcomes-gpl-java.html). Free Software Foundation. November 15, 2006. . Retrieved 2007-09-23. "FSF president and founder Richard Stallman said, "I think Sun has contributed more than any other company to the free software community in the form of software. It shows leadership. It's an example I hope others will follow.""

[8]   "The SUN Workstation Architecture" (ftp://reports.stanford.edu/pub/cstr/reports/csl/tr/82/229/CSL-TR-82-229.pdf). *Stanford University Computer systems Laboratory Technical Report No. 229*. March 1982. . Retrieved 2009-07-28.

[9]   "Wellspring of Innovation: Sun Microsystems Spotlight" (http://www.stanford.edu/group/wellspring/sun_spotlight.html). Stanford.edu. . Retrieved 2009-07-28.

[10] Harvard.edu (http://harvardbusinessonline.hbsp.harvard.edu/b02/en/common/item_detail.jhtml?id=390049), Vinod Khosla and Sun Microsystems, Amar Bhide, Harvard Business School, 12/14/89

[11] "Mr. Scott McNealy" (http://www.sun.com/products-n-solutions/edu/gelc/bios/scottmcnealy.html). Sun Microsystems, Inc.. 2005-04-24. . Retrieved 2009-09-17.

[12] Jim McGuinness (August 27, 2007). "Jim McGuinness's Weblog" (http://blogs.sun.com/dador/entry/ sunw_stanford_university_network_workstation). . Retrieved 2009-02-22.

[13] "Sun goes back to the future with Metropolis" (http://www.theregister.co.uk/2004/06/02/sun_shows_metropolis/). The Register. 2 June 2004. . Retrieved 2007-01-31.

[14] "Sun Microsystems — Investor Relations: FAQ" (http://www.sun.com/aboutsun/investor/faq/#04). Sun Microsystems, Inc.. . Retrieved 2007-01-23.

[15] By Alexei Oreskovic (2007-08-23). "Sun to Switch Symbol to JAVA" (http://www.thestreet.com/_yahoo/newsanalysis/techhardware/
10376053.html?cm_ven=YAHOO&cm_cat=FREE&cm_ite=NA). Thestreet.com. . Retrieved 2009-07-28.

[16] http://www.thenetworkisthecomputer.com/

[17] "NASDAQ" (http://quotes.nasdaq.com/quote.dll?page=charting&mode=basics&intraday=off&timeframe=10y&charttype=ohlc&
splits=off&earnings=off&movingaverage=None&lowerstudy=volume&comparison=off&index=&drilldown=off&symbol=SUNW&
selected=SUNW). Quotes.nasdaq.com. . Retrieved 2009-07-28.

[18] Shankland, Stephen (18 September 2003). "Sun to lay off 1,000" (http://news.com.com/Sun+to+lay+off+1,000/
2100-1022_3-5078493.html). CNet News.com. . Retrieved 2007-07-13.

[19] Vance, Ashlee (24 June 2005). "Sun layoffs hit hundreds in US" (http://www.theregister.co.uk/2005/06/24/sun_layoffs_2006/). The
Register. . Retrieved 2007-07-13.

[20] Shankland, Stephen (7 April 2006). "Sun layoffs hit high-end server group" (http://web.archive.org/web/20070210194319/http://news.
zdnet.com/2100-1009_22-6058894.html). ZDNet. Archived from the original (http://news.zdnet.com/2100-1009_22-6058894.html) on
February 10, 2007. . Retrieved 2007-07-13.

[21] "Sun to add jobs in Hillsboro" (http://www.bizjournals.com/portland/stories/2004/01/12/daily49.html). Portland Business Journal. 16
January 2004. . Retrieved 2007-07-14.

[22] "Sun to sell Newark campus, move 2,300 workers" (http://sanjose.bizjournals.com/sanjose/stories/2006/05/08/daily55.html). Silicon
Valley, San Jose Business Journal. 11 May 2006. . Retrieved 2007-07-14.

[23] "CDO2 Unlocks The Power of Sun Grid for Faster Financial Risk Simulation" (http://www.prnewswire.com/cgi-bin/stories.
pl?ACCT=104&STORY=/www/story/08-24-2005/0004093251&EDATE=). 24 August 2005. .

[24] "Sun Microsystems Welcomes Endorsement and Investment From KKR" (http://www.prnewswire.com/cgi-bin/stories.pl?ACCT=104&
STORY=/www/story/01-23-2007/0004511496). 23 January 2007. .

[25] "Offshoring Software Development presentation by Sun to the aECD" (http://www.oecd.org/dataoecd/32/9/37846828.pdf) (PDF). .

[26] Ashlee Vance, "Crisis Hits Tech Sector With Layoffs as Sales Slump," New York Times, Nov. 14, 2008 (http://www.nytimes.com/2008/
11/15/technology/companies/15sun.html?_r=1&hp&oref=slogin)

[27] "Trancept Systems" (http://www.dotcsw.com/trancept.html). . Retrieved 2007-05-12.

[28] Sun Microsystems (September 6, 1988). "Sun Microsystems Acquires Folio, Inc." (http://groups.google.com/group/comp.windows.
news/msg/6b21cd36461d711d). Press release. . Retrieved 2007-11-12.

[29] "Sun's SunSelect Acquires Windows-Under-Unix Emulation Firm Praxsys" (http://www.cbronline.com/news/
suns_sunselect_acquires_windows_under_unix_emulation_firm_praxsys). Computergram. 1992-09-18. . Retrieved 2009-04-03.

[30] "Sun pitches software savvy as it pushes past server identity" (http://www.bizjournals.com/sanjose/stories/2002/06/03/smallb2.html).
San Jose Business Journal. 2002-05-31. .

[31] Sun Microsystems (May 17, 1996). "Sun Mycrosystems announces intent to purchase Cray Business Systems Division" (http://www.sun.
com/smi/Press/sunflash/1996-05/sunflash.960517.4027.xml). Press release. . Retrieved 2007-03-10.

[32] "Sun Microsystems, Inc. acqquires Longview Technologies LLC" (http://www.sun.com/smi/Press/sunflash/1997-02/sunflash.970218.
8791.xml). 18 February 1997. .

[33] "Sun Microsystems completes acquisition of DIBA, pioneer in information appliance industry" (http://www.sun.com/smi/Press/
sunflash/1997-08/sunflash.970825.10.xml). 25 August 1997. .

[34] Sun Microsystems, Inc. (September 10, 1997). "Sun expands network software business to embedded systems market; agrees to acquire
Chorus Systems" (http://www.sun.com/smi/Press/sunflash/1997-09/sunflash.970910.1.xml). Press release. . Retrieved 2007-05-13.

[35] "Sun Microsystems signs definitive agreement to acquire Encore Computer's storage business" (http://www.sun.com/smi/Press/sunflash/
1997-07/sunflash.970717.1112.xml). 17 July 1997. .

[36] "Will a big company buy your startup?" (http://sanjose.bizjournals.com/sanfrancisco/stories/1998/07/20/smallb2.html). San
Francisco Business Times. .

[37] "Sun buys NetDynamics" (http://news.com.com/Sun+buys+NetDynamics/2100-1001_3-212908.html). CNET. July 1, 1998. .

[38] "Sun snaps up software company Gridware" (http://news.com.com/Sun+snaps+up+software+company+Gridware/
2100-1001_3-243555.html). CNET. 24 July 2000. . Retrieved 2007-05-18.

[39] "Sun Takes a Shine to Cobalt" (http://www.internetnews.com/fina-news/article.php/5_463841). Internetnews.com. 19 September 2000.
. Retrieved 2007-05-18.

[40] "Sun snags storage company, software maker" (http://news.com.com/Sun+snags+storage+company,+software+maker/
2100-1001_3-249318.html?tag=item). CNET News.com. 4 December 2000. . Retrieved 2007-07-04.

[41] "Sun buys Clustra for iPlanet" (http://www.information-age.com/article/2002/march/sun_buys_clustra_for_iplanet). InformationAge.
19 March 2002. . Retrieved 2007-07-04.

[42] "Sun buys start-up to boost UltraSparc" (http://news.com.com/Sun+buys+start-up+to+boost+UltraSparc/2100-1001_3-939307.html).
CNET News.com. 25 June 2002. . Retrieved 2007-07-04.

[43] "Sun to buy start-up to boost 'N1' plan" (http://news.com.com/2100-1001-958610.html). CNET News.com. 19 September 2002. .
Retrieved 2007-07-04.

[44] "Sun springs for software maker" (http://news.com.com/Sun+springs+for+software+maker/2100-1001_3-965980.html). CNET
News.com. 15 November 2002. . Retrieved 2007-07-04.

[45] "Sun Microsystems To Acquire Pixo" (http://www.techweb.com/wire/showArticle.jhtml?articleID=26801457). TechWeb. 26 June 2003. . Retrieved 2007-07-04.

[46] "Sun Facts Acquisitions History" (http://www.sun.com/aboutsun/investor/sun_facts/merger_history.jsp). Sun Microsystems Inc.. August 2003. .

[47] Sun Microsystems (December 10, 2003). "Sun completes acquisition of Waveset Technologies, Inc." (http://www.sun.com/smi/Press/sunflash/2003-12/sunflash.20031210.1.xml). Press release. . Retrieved 2007-01-01.

[48] "Sun Microsystems enhances network services integration into blades platform; Signs agreement to acquire Nauticus Networks" (http://www.sun.com/smi/Press/sunflash/2004-01/sunflash.20040120.2.xml). 2 January 2004. .

[49] "Sun to buy Opteron server maker, reclaim co-founder" (http://news.com.com/2100-1010_3-5156828.html). CNET. 10 February 2004. . Retrieved 2007-07-04.

[50] Sun Microsystems (11 January 2005). "Sun Completes Acquisition Of Sevenspace" (http://www.sun.com/smi/Press/sunflash/2005-01/sunflash.20050111.1.xml). Press release. . Retrieved 2007-10-03.

[51] "Sun to buy Tarantella" (http://news.com.com/Sun+to+buy+Tarantella/2100-1012_3-5701487.html?tag=item). CNET. 10 May 2005. . Retrieved 2007-07-04.

[52] "Sun to buy integration outfit SeeBeyond" (http://news.com.com/Sun+to+buy+integration+outfit+SeeBeyond/2100-1014_3-5766116.html?tag=item). CNET. 28 June 2005. . Retrieved 2007-07-04.

[53] "Sun Facts Acquisitions History" (http://www.sun.com/aboutsun/investor/sun_facts/merger_history.jsp). Sun Microsystems Inc.. June 2005. .

[54] "Sun Microsystems Completes Acquisition of StorageTek" (http://www.sun.com/smi/Press/sunflash/2005-08/sunflash.20050831.1.xml). August 31, 2005. .

[55] Sun Microsystems, Inc. (February 22, 2006). "Sun to Acquire Aduva" (http://www.sun.com/smi/Press/sunflash/2006-02/sunflash.20060222.2.xml). Press release. . Retrieved 2007-05-17.

[56] Sun Microsystems, Inc. (September 27, 2006). "Sun to Bolster Identity Management Leadership and Service Offerings With Acquisition of Neogent" (http://www.sun.com/smi/Press/sunflash/2006-09/sunflash.20060927.1.xml). Press release. . Retrieved 2007-11-13.

[57] Sun Microsystems, Inc. (September 12, 2007). "Sun Microsystems Expands High Performance Computing Portfolio with Definitive Agreement to Acquire Assets of Cluster File Systems, Including the Lustre File System" (http://www.sun.com/aboutsun/pr/2007-09/sunflash.20070912.2.xml). Press release. . Retrieved 2007-09-13.

[58] Sun Microsystems, Inc. (November 13, 2007). "Sun Microsystems Strengthens Market-Leading Identity Management Portfolio with Intent to Acquire Vaau" (http://www.sun.com/aboutsun/pr/2007-11/sunflash.20071113.2.xml). Press release. . Retrieved 2007-11-13.

[59] Sun Microsystems, Inc. (February 26, 2008). "Sun Microsystems Announces Completion of MySQL Acquisition; Paves Way for Secure, Open Source Platform to Power the Network Economy" (http://www.sun.com/aboutsun/pr/2008-02/sunflash.20080226.1.xml). Press release. . Retrieved 2008-02-26.

[60] Sun Microsystems, Inc. (February 12, 2008). "Sun Microsystems Announces Agreement to Acquire innotek, Expanding Sun xVM Reach to the Developer Desktop" (http://www.sun.com/aboutsun/pr/2008-02/sunflash.20080212.1.xml). Press release. . Retrieved 2008-02-12.

[61] "Sun Welcomes Innotek" (http://www.sun.com/software/innotek/). Sun Microsystems, Inc.. . Retrieved 2008-02-26. "On February 20 Sun completed the acquisition of innotek"

[62] Sun Microsystems, Inc. (January 6, 2009). "Sun Microsystems Expands Cloud Computing Offerings with Acquisition of Q-layer" (http://www.sun.com/aboutsun/pr/2009-01/sunflash.20090107.1.xml). Press release. . Retrieved 2009-01-06.

[63] "Preliminary merger proxy statement" (http://sec.gov/Archives/edgar/data/709519/000119312509107681/dprem14a.htm#toc42384_46) By Sun Micro

[64] Sun Microsystems (http://www.sun.com/nc/05q3/videos/index.jsp?exec=3)

[65] Sun Microsystems (January 22, 2007). "Sun And Intel Announce Landmark Agreement" (http://www.sun.com/aboutsun/pr/2007-01/sunflash.20070122.1.xml). Press release. . Retrieved 2007-01-23.

[66] YouTube (April 30, 2008). "OpenSolaris & Intel Xeon Processors" (http://www.youtube.com/watch?v=VIb8VIg0JM0). Press release. . Retrieved 2008-05-12.

[67] AMD (May 5, 2008). "AMD Expands Charter for the OpenSolaris OS and Sun xVM at the AMD Operating System Research Center" (http://www.amd.com/gb-uk/Corporate/VirtualPressRoom/0,,51_104_543~125446,00.html). Press release. .

[68] Rishab Aiyer Ghosh (November 20, 2006). "Study on the: Economic impact of open source software on innovation and the competitiveness of the Information and Communication Technologies (ICT) sector in the EU" (http://ec.europa.eu/enterprise/ict/policy/doc/2006-11-20-flossimpact.pdf) (PDF). European Union. pp. 51. . Retrieved 2007-01-25.

[69] John, Burgess (January 7, 1988). "AT&T to Buy Stake In Sun Microsystems" (http://pqasb.pqarchiver.com/washingtonpost_historical/access/406816581.html?dids=406816581:406816581&FMT=ABS&FMTS=ABS:FT&date=JAN+07,+1988&author=John+Burgess+Washington+Post+Staff+Writer&pub=The+Washington+Post). *The Washington Post*. . Retrieved 2007-01-23. "American Telephone & Telegraph Co. announced yesterday that it will buy up a 20 percent stake in Sun Microsystems Inc., a Silicon Valley-based maker of powerful small computers known as workstations."

[70] Microsoft Corporation, Sun Microsystems, Inc. (April 2, 2004). "Microsoft and Sun Microsystems Enter Broad Cooperation Agreement; Settle Outstanding Litigation" (http://web.archive.org/web/20060322045711/http://www.sun.com/smi/Press/sunflash/2004-04/sunflash.20040402.3.xml). Press release. Archived from the original (http://www.sun.com/smi/Press/sunflash/2004-04/sunflash.20040402.3.xml) on 2006-03-22. . Retrieved 2008-06-16.

[71] Mary Jo Foley (September 12, 2007). "Microsoft and Sun agree to support each other in virtualized environments" (http://blogs.zdnet.
com/microsoft/?p=712). *ZDNet*. . Retrieved 2008-02-06.

[72] "[[TIOBE Programming Community Index (http://www.tiobe.com/tpci.htm)]"]. TIOBE Software. June 2007. . Retrieved 2007-07-05.
Java is ranked 1st as of June 2007, and has ranked 1st or 2nd in this index since its inception in 2001.

[73] "Sun Opens Java" (http://web.archive.org/web/20070124154133/http://www.sun.com/2006-1113/feature/story.jsp). *Sun
Microsystems Web site*. 13 November 2006. Archived from the original (http://www.sun.com/2006-1113/feature/story.jsp) on January 24,
2007. . Retrieved 2007-01-25.

[74] Brandon Bailey (February 20, 2009). "Sun Microsystems, Adobe, Microsoft will battle for dominance in Internet software" (http://www.
mercurynews.com/breakingnews/ci_11741973). *San Jose Mercury News*. . Retrieved 2009-03-02.

[75] "Product Comparison" (http://www.sun.com/software/star/openoffice/). *Sun Microsystems*. . Retrieved 2008-09-18.

[76] "Sun Microsystems to acquire Innotek" (http://www.forbes.com/feeds/afx/2008/02/12/afx4645428.html). *Forbes*. February 12, 2008.
.

[77] "Helping Dolphins Fly" (http://blogs.sun.com/jonathan/entry/winds_of_change_are_blowing). Sun Microsystems. January 16, 2008. .
Retrieved 2008-02-28.

[78] "Optimize MySQL Server on Sun x64 Servers and Storage" (http://www.sun.com/blueprints/0208/820-4498.html). Sun Microsystems.
February 2008. . Retrieved 2008-02-28.

[79] Sun Microsystems (January 25, 2000). "Sun-Netscape alliance targets e-commerce with new brand identity" (http://www.sun.com/smi/
Press/sunflash/2000-01/sunflash.20000125.5.xml). Press release. . Retrieved 2007-01-01.

[80] "OpenSolaris Project: HoneyComb Fixed Content Storage" (http://opensolaris.org/os/project/honeycomb/). Sun Microsystems. February
2008. . Retrieved 2008-02-28.

[81] "Solaris ZFS Enables Hybrid Storage Pools: Shatters Economic and Performance Barriers" (http://www.sun.com/x64/intel/
zfs_solution_brief.pdf). Sun Microsystems. . Retrieved 2009-04-09.

[82] "Lustre File System presentation" (http://video.google.ca/videoplay?docid=965817030102279091). *Google Video*. . Retrieved
2008-01-28.

[83] "OpenSolaris Project: HPC Stack" (http://opensolaris.org/os/project/hpc-stack/). Sun Microsystems. . Retrieved 2008-08-07.

[84] "Blogs.sun.com" (http://blogs.sun.com). *Sun Microsystems*. .

[85] Konrad, Rachel (16 September 2006). "Sun CEO Among the Few Chiefs Who Blog" (http://www.washingtonpost.com/wp-dyn/content/
article/2006/09/16/AR2006091600257.html). *The Washington Post*. . Retrieved 2007-07-04.

[86] Jones, Del (26 June 2006). "Sun CEO sees competitive advantage in blogging" (http://www.usatoday.com/tech/news/
2006-06-25-exec-sun_x.htm). *USA Today*. . Retrieved 2007-07-04.

[87] "Jason Stamper's Blog: The ROI of blogging, and whether Jonathan Schwartz's blog pays for itself" (http://www.businessreviewonline.
com/blog/archives/2006/04/the_roi_of_blog.html). *Computer Business Review Online*. 4 April 2006. . Retrieved 2007-07-04.

Further reading

- Hall, Mark; Barry, John (1990). *Sunburst: The Ascent of Sun Microsystems*. Chicago: Contemporary Books.
  ISBN 0-8092-3989-2. OCLC 232948325.
- Southwick, Karen (1999). *High Noon: The Inside Story of Scott McNealy and the Rise of Sun Microsystems* (http:/
  /ca.wiley.com/WileyCDA/WileyTitle/productCd-0471297135.html). New York: John Wiley.
  ISBN 0-471-29713-5. OCLC 41404354.

External links

- Official website (http://http://www.oracle.com/sun)
- Sun Microsystems (http://www.dmoz.org/Computers/Companies/Sun_Microsystems/) at the Open Directory
  Project
- "System news for Sun Users" (http://sun.systemnews.com). *Sun Microsystems*. - A weekly summary of news
  about Sun and its products now in its 10th year.

List of display interfaces

This is a **list of physical video connectors** and related **video signal standards**. For other video-related standards, please see the main article, video.

By signal standard

Signal standard name	Year introduced	Connector	Analog or digital	Max resolution (X-pix x Y-pix @ Hz)	Used for	Notes
Composite video	1956 [1]	1 RCA, BNC, TV Aerial Plug, or Mini-VGA	Analog	720 x 576i @ 50 720 x 480i @ 59.94	Consumer electronics, including VCR and LaserDisc, 1970-1980s home computers like the Commodore VIC-20, 1980s-1990s video game consoles, some laptops	Used with PAL, NTSC or SECAM color.
S-Video (Separate-Video or Y/C)	1979	1 Mini-DIN 4 pin, 1 Mini-VGA, 2 BNC, 2 RCA connectors	Analog	720 x 576i @ 50 720 x 480i @ 59.94	S-VHS, some laptop computers, analog broadcast video, 1980-1990s home computers including the Commodore C64, C128 and Atari 8-bit	The 4-pin mini-DIN that is most common in consumer products today debuted in JVC's 1987 S-VHS. Used with PAL, NTSC or SECAM color. Where two connectors are used, they are labeled *Chroma* and *Luma*.
SCART	1977	SCART 21-pin	Analog	720 x 576i @ 50 720 x 480i @ 59.94	Consumer electronics, Commodore-Amiga and various video games	Europe "unified" A/V interface for composite video, composite sync + RGB, audio and S-video. Composite and s-video are used with PAL, NTSC or SECAM color.
CGA	1981	DE-9	Digital	640 x 200 @ 60	Pre-i80386 x86 machines	
MDA	1981	DE-9	Digital	720 x 350 @ 50, Text only		
HGC	1982	DE-9[2]	Digital	720 x 348 @ 50		
EGA	1984	DE-9	Digital	640 x 350 @ 60		
Amiga video	1985	DB23	Both, GenLock	1280 x 400/512 @ 60/50	Commodore-Amiga	Similar to SCART, but also includes a digital RGBI signal, Genlock clock, composite sync and +12/+5VDC power [3]

VGA	1987	VGA connector variants include DE-15/HD-15 (canonical), DE-9, RGB or RGBHV on separate BNC connectors, Mini-VGA, DVI/Mini-DVI/Micro-DVI.	Analog	2048 x 1536 @ 85 [4]	Introduced with IBM x86 machines, but became a universal analog display interface. Display Data Channel was later added to allow monitors to identify themselves to graphic cards, and graphic cards to modify monitor settings.	Successor analog protocols include SVGA, XGA, etc. DVI is a more modern digital alternative. Where BNC is used, available as 3 connectors with *Sync on Green*, or 5 connector Red / Green / Blue / Horizontal Sync / Vertical sync.
Mac-II/Quadra	1987	DA15F	Analog	1152 x 870 @ 75 [5]	Macintosh	Mac-DA15F and Sun-13W3 were similar in capability to VGA. Some Sun machines used 4 or 5 BNC connectors to transfer video signal.
13W3	1990	DB13W3	Analog	1152 x 900 @ 76	Sun computer systems	
OpenLDI	1998	MDR36	LVDS Digital			
Component video	1990s	3 RCA or BNC	Analog	1920×1080 @ 60 1280×720 @ 60 720×480 @ 60	consumer electronics	Usually YPbPr
D-Terminal	1990s	Apple-AAUI	Analog	1920×1080 @ 60	Japanese consumer electronics	Uses component video and resolution selection via voltage levels.
Digital Visual Interface (DVI)	1999	DVI, Mini-DVI, Micro-DVI	Both	2560 x 1600 @ 60 3840 × 2400 @ 33	Recent video cards	Almost a ubiquitous computer display link. Uncompressed video only. High-bandwidth Digital Content Protection (HDCP). Encryption is optional.
ADC	2000	Apple-ADC	Both	2560 x 1600 @ 60	Apple Inc. Macintoshes and monitors	Proprietary connector with DVI signals
High-Definition Multimedia Interface (HDMI)	2003	HDMI Type A/C	Digital	2560 x 1600 @ 75 4096 × 2160 @ 24	Many A/V systems and video cards (including motherboards with IGP)	High-bandwidth Digital Content Protection (HDCP). Encryption is mandatory.
DisplayPort	2007	20-pin (external) 32-pin (internal)	Digital	2560 x 1600 @ 75	Apple Inc. and Dell monitors ATI *RV670* based graphics cards and NVIDIA *G92* graphics cards (both as OEM optional implementations)	DisplayPort introduced the 128bit-AES to replace HDCP. DisplayPort version 1.1 added support for HDCP.

| Serial Digital Interface | | BNC | | Digital | From 143 Mbit/s to 2.970 Gbit/s, depending on variant. 480i, 576i, 480p, 576p, 720p, 1080i, 1080p. | Broadcast video. Variants include SD-SDI, HD-SDI, Dual Link HD-SDI, 3G-SDI. | |

Physical connectors

Image	Class or connector name	Used for	Notes
RF connectors (analog radio frequency signals). Generally use coaxial cable types such as RG-6 and RG-59 (except for twin-lead).			
Belling-Lee connector / IEC 169-2 connector	TV aerial plug, (a.k.a. PAL connector in Europe)	Most video devices in the world (other than the United States) connected directly to a roof antenna. Used by early home computers and game consoles to connect them to TVs because of the lack of any other connector.	Generally not used in the United States.
	BNC (*Bayonet Neill-Concelman*)	Alternative to RCA for professional video electronics. Protocols: Serial Digital Interface (SDI) and HD-SDI.	75 Ω for video signal on, for example, RG59 e RG6. 50 Ω for data link, like Ethernet on RG58. 93 Ω on RG62.
50Ω (white/bottom row) and 75Ω C connectors (red/top row)	C connector (*Concelman connector*)		

		GR connector (*General Radio* connector)		
		F connector	Used for U.S. TV antenna installations (but not for TV antenna installations outside of the US), satellite and cable systems worldwide. Also common in U.S. for early home computers & game consoles, older VCRs, RF modulators, and even CECBs due to lack of other connectors.	
		N connector (*Neill* connector)		
TNC connector (left), compared with BNC (right)		Threaded Neill-Concelman connector (TNC)		
		Twin-lead	Used for older TV antenna installations in the U.S. and various other countries worldwide. Current use generally limited to baluns to adapt 300Ω twin-lead to/from 75Ω F connector.	Replaced by F connector in the US and Belling-Lee Connector in other countries outside the U.S.

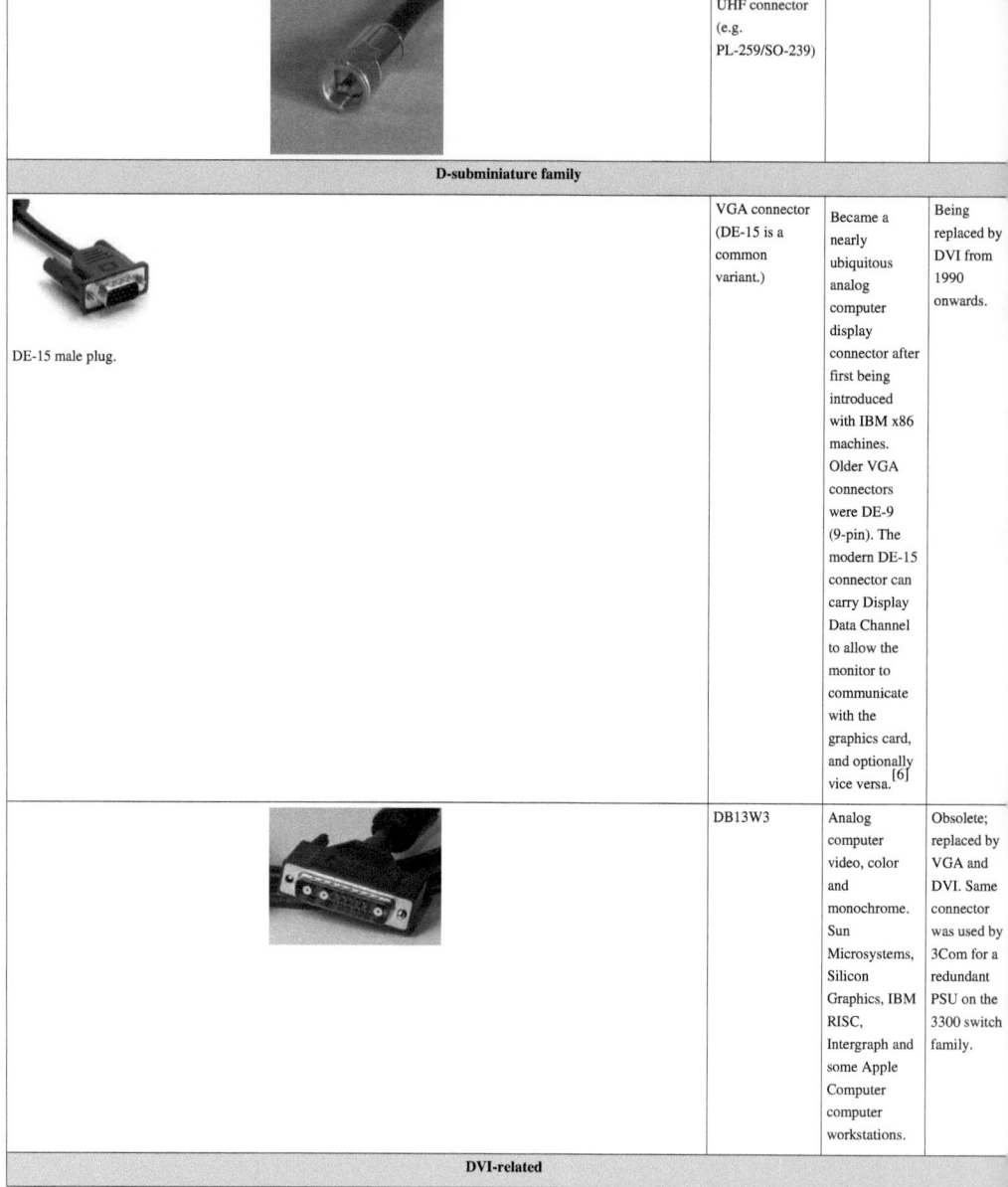

		UHF connector (e.g. PL-259/SO-239)		
D-subminiature family				
DE-15 male plug.		VGA connector (DE-15 is a common variant.)	Became a nearly ubiquitous analog computer display connector after first being introduced with IBM x86 machines. Older VGA connectors were DE-9 (9-pin). The modern DE-15 connector can carry Display Data Channel to allow the monitor to communicate with the graphics card, and optionally vice versa.[6]	Being replaced by DVI from 1990 onwards.
		DB13W3	Analog computer video, color and monochrome. Sun Microsystems, Silicon Graphics, IBM RISC, Intergraph and some Apple Computer computer workstations.	Obsolete; replaced by VGA and DVI. Same connector was used by 3Com for a redundant PSU on the 3300 switch family.
DVI-related				

Single-link DVI-D male plug. Dual-link DVI-D male plug.	Digital Visual Interface (DVI). 5 variants are: DVI-I single link, DVI-I dual link, DVI-D single link, DVI-D dual link, and DVI-A.	Almost ubiquitous for modern computer video cards.	
Male Mini-DVI plug on top of a 12-inch PowerBook G4; female port is second from left.	Mini-DVI	VGA, DVI, television. Apple Computer alternative to Mini-VGA.	
Female Micro-DVI port (rightmost) on MacBook Air	Micro-DVI	DVI-D dual link	
	DMS-59	DVI dual link	
	Apple Display Connector	Combines DVI, USB, and power.	
One of the 3 HDMI variants, male plug.	High-Definition Multimedia Interface (HDMI)	High definition digital video devices (HDMI protocol)	Electrically compatible with DVI-D and DVD-I, using a simple adapter.
DIN/Mini-DIN			
	Mini-DIN 4-pin	S-Video (Separate-Video or Y/C)	
	Various Mini-DIN configurations	Various systems and protocols - see Mini-DIN for details	
Others			

3 RCA connectors - yellow for composite video, and white and red for stereo audio	RCA connector	Widely used in consumer electronics for audio and video.	A single connector must be used for each signal.
	SCART	Consumer electronics, mostly in Europe. Carries stereophonic audio (analog), along with either composite video or RGB video. Some devices support S-Video sharing the same pins as composite video and RGB.	
D4 video connector	D-Terminal	Popular in Japan for analog high definition video. Available sizes are D1 through D5.	Replacing RCA connectors.
Male Mini-VGA plug on top of an Apple laptop, female port is second from right.	Mini-VGA (used for laptops)	Used for laptops, especially from Apple Computer and some from Sony.	
AV Multi (gold-plated male plugs)	AV Multi	Sony proprietary. Combines composite video, S-Video, RGB, component video, and stereophonic sound (two analog channels).	

	35-pin MicroCross Molex connector	VESA Enhanced Video Connector and VESA Plug and Display (a.k.a. M1-DA) both used this connector with slightly different pin assignments. These schemes combined VGA or digital video, audio, FireWire, and USB signals into a single connector.	Defunct, obsoleted by DFP and later DVI
	HDI-45	Apple proprietary. Combines Analog VGA out, stereo analog audio out, analog microphone in, S-video capture in, Apple desktop bus interface	Proprietary connector used on Apple Macintosh Centris computers, and the Apple AudioVision 14 Display. An attempt by Apple to deal with cable clutter, by combining five separate cables from computer to monitor.
Female port (20-pin)	Digital Flat Panel	Used with the PanelLink digital video protocol.	Obsoleted by DVI
	Unified Display Interface		Proposed to replace both DVI and HDMI. Deprecated by Intel in favor of DisplayPort.

		3.5mm (⅛") TRRS and TRS connector	Analog camcorders commonly use a 3.5mm 4-contact TRRS connector to carry composite video and stereo audio.	Jack appears identical to more common 3-contact stereo audio-only (Walkman) 3.5mm TRS connector.
		DisplayPort	DisplayPort is also the name of the protocol, which is proposed to replace DVI for computer monitors, and consumer electronics (such as home theatre systems).	
Male Mini DisplayPort plug		Mini DisplayPort	Proposed alternative to HDMI, used with computer displays: (VGA, DVI) Apple Inc.'s successor to their own Mini-DVI.	

References

[1] "What is CVBS video format - aus.tv.pay" (http://groups.google.se/group/aus.tv.pay/browse_thread/thread/9fac4a26de804841/f59fa50df0338f35?lnk=st&q=CVBS++"Fernseh"++channel+nine+air++1956&rnum=1&hl=sv#f59fa50df0338f35). *Google-grupper*. . 070824 groups.google.se

[2] "The PC video acronyms" (http://philipstorr.id.au/pcbook/book3/videstan.htm). . 070820 philipstorr.id.au

[3] "Amiga video pinout" (http://pinouts.ru/Video/AmigaVideo_pinout.shtml). . pinouts.ru

[4] 2560 x 1600 @ 60 Hz in theory (http://www.nvidia.com/page/quadroplex_tech_specs.html), although few existing WQXGA device offers analog inputs (certain Barco projectors do)

[5] Capable of higher on later Macintosh models if used with the right equipment, i.e. a DA15F to VGA converter coupled with a sufficiently capable analog display

[6] VGA pinout and signals @ pinouts.ru (http://pinouts.ru/Video/VGA15_pinout.shtml)

External links

- Monitor Ports (http://whitefiles.org/b1_s/1_free_guides/fg1mt/pgs/h10f.htm) Pinouts and other technical information; lacks more recent interfaces such as HDMI
- PC Graphics standard overview (http://epanorama.net/documents/pc/pc_graphics.html) Simple table of PC video standards thru XGA with DB9 pinouts
- Summary of Video Standards (http://www.monitorworld.com/Cables/video_standards.html) up to XGA
- Standard and device-specific video interfaces pinouts (http://pinouts.ru/pin_Video.shtml) Numerous standards described and categorized, including such recent ones as DVI and HDMI
- List of computer video standards and connectors pinouts (http://www.allpinouts.org/index.php/ Category:Computer_Video_Connectors) Wiki format (including community updates and free redistribution); broad coverage including HDMI

Sun acquisition by Oracle

The acquisition of Sun Microsystems by Oracle Corporation was completed by Oracle on January 27, 2010.[1]

History

In late 2008, Sun was approached by IBM to discuss a possible merger.[2] At about the same time, Sun also began discussions with another company, widely rumored but unconfirmed to be Hewlett Packard, about a potential acquisition. By March of 2009, talks had stalled between Sun and both IBM and the other potential suitor.

On April 20, 2009, Sun and Oracle Corporation announced that they had entered into a definitive agreement under which Oracle would acquire Sun for $9.50 a share in cash. Net of Sun's cash and debt, this amounts to a $5.6 billion dollar offer from Oracle. Sun's shareholders voted to approve the proposal on July 16, 2009, although the deal was still subject to regulatory approvals.[3] Terms of the agreement between Oracle and Sun included dependencies on the antitrust laws of "the United States and Canada, European Union, China, Israel, Switzerland, Russia, Australia, Turkey, Korea, Japan, Mexico and South Africa".[4]

On August 20, 2009, it was reported that the U.S. government, pursuant to the Clayton Antitrust Act, approved Oracle's purchase of Sun.[5]

On September 3, 2009, the European Commission announced that it would not immediately approve the deal, but would instead perform a second round of investigation, focusing on the implications of Oracle's control of MySQL (acquired by Sun in 2008).[6]

On October 20, 2009, Sun filed with the U.S. Securities and Exchange Commission (SEC) its intention to cut 3,000 jobs globally over next 12 months, citing losses caused by delays in the acquisition process.[7]

On November 6, in its 10-Q filing for the 1st quarter of the 2010 fiscal year, Sun announced 25% total revenue decrease, compared to the 1st quarter of the previous year, due to "economic downturn, the uncertainty associated with our proposed acquisition by Oracle, increased competition and delays in customer purchasing decisions".[8]

On January 21, 2010, EU Competition Commissioner Neelie Kroes announced unconditional approval of the deal.[9]

On January 27, 2010, Oracle announced that it had completed its acquisition of Sun Microsystems, making Sun a wholly owned subsidiary of Oracle.

Impact

Solaris changes

Solaris 10 license change

The Solaris 10 download license changed to limit unpaid use to 90 days (http:/ / www. infoworld. com/ d/ open-source/ license-change-leaves-sun-solaris-users-crossroads-858?page=0,0) (http:/ / www. theinquirer. net/ inquirer/news/1599130/oracle-cut-sun-source).

OpenSolaris omission from roadmaps, Open letter to Oracle, and EOL documents

After OpenSolaris was omitted from Oracle Product roadmaps [10] , core OpenSolaris developer Ben Rockwood wrote an Open Letter to Oracle about the direction of the project[11] which as of 2010-02-25 had not been responded to by Oracle. More recently, End of Life Documents for OpenSolaris were published on Oracle's website[12] which had not previously existed.[13] A statement from Oracle Vice President of Corporate Communications Letty Ledbetter responded "Keep it movin', folks ... nothing to see here. The page is a policy page to describe how the service life of the product works. [We're] not announcing EOL [for OpenSolaris]."[14]

OpenSolaris 2010.03

OpenSolaris's scheduled 2010.03 release did not occur as of 31 March 2010. As of that time, Oracle has not provided any information from the corporate level on the release time change, nor is it clear that the acquisition had any direct bearing on the date change, as OpenSolaris developers have indicated that this was largely due to a number of show-stopping bugs that had not been resolved.

Hardware Support Requirement for Software Support

Oracle has changed the software support model to also require hardware support. The new policy states "when acquiring technical support, all hardware systems must be supported (e.g., Oracle Premier Support for Systems or Oracle Premier Support for Operating Systems) or unsupported." (http:/ / www. cio. com/ article/ 588163/ Oracle_Enacts_all_Or_Nothing_Hardware_Support_Policy?page=1&taxonomyId=3045)

Product Team resignations

Notable Engineer resignations

Java

James Gosling, the creator of Java, resigned in April 2010.

XML

Tim Bray, the creator of XML, resigned in April 2009 and moved to Google.

DTrace

Bryan Cantrill, the co-creator of DTrace, resigned in July 2010.

JRuby team

While the deal was still pending regulatory approval, the JRuby team collectively resigned from Sun and moved to Engine Yard. [15]

Drizzle team

The Drizzle DBMS team collectively resigned from Sun and moved to Rackspace. [16]

Executive resignations

Most of Sun's executive management team, including CEO Jonathan Schwartz, resigned immediately after the acquisition was complete. John Fowler, Executive VP of Sun's systems group, remained at Oracle as Executive Vice President of Hardware Engineering.[17]

Simon Phipps, Sun's Chief Open Source Officer, quit on March 8, 2010.[18]

Director resignations

Tim Bray

Tim Bray, Sun's Director of Web Technologies, moved to Google.

Program closures

Project Kenai

Project Kenai, a Sourceforge-like project for Java apps, was migrated to Java.net by Oracle. [19]

DarkStar

Project Darkstar, a project to investigate and create solutions for issues in massive online gaming environments, was closed by Oracle on February 2, 2010 [20] [21] .

MySQL petition and forks

A major issue discussed in media and considered by the EU Competition Commission was Oracle's acquisition of MySQL, an open-source competitor to Oracle acquired by Sun in February 2008, as part of the deal.

In response, several forks were made with the intent to ensure the future success of MySQL despite being purchased by its biggest competitor. These include Drizzle and MariaDB. Monty Widenius, one of the founders of MySQL, also started a petition asking that MySQL either be divested to a third party, or have its licensing changed to be less restrictive than the previous GPL terms it operated under prior to and during its ownership by Sun.[22]

References

[1] "Oracle Completes Acquisition of Sun" (http://finance.yahoo.com/news/Oracle-Completes-Acquisition-iw-2658323391.html?x=0&. v=1). Yahoo. 27 January 2010. . Retrieved 27 January 2010.

[2] Alex Handy (July 16, 2009). "Proxy reveals three-way competition over ownership of Sun" (http://www.sdtimes.com/link/33610). *SD Times*. . Retrieved 2010-01-30.

[3] "Sun Microsystems Announces Stockholder Approval of Oracle Merger Agreement" (http://www.sun.com/aboutsun/pr/2009-07/ sunflash.20090716.1.xml). Sun Microsystems. July 16, 2009. . Retrieved 2009-07-16.

[4] Sun Microsystems (June 8, 2009). "Definitive Merger Proxy" (http://www.sec.gov/Archives/edgar/data/709519/000119312509126389/ ddefm14a.htm). *EDGAR*. United States Securities and Exchange Commission. . Retrieved 2010-01-30.

[5] Thomasch, Paul (August 20, 2009). "Oracle wins U.S. approval to buy Sun Microsystems" (http://www.reuters.com/article/ rbssTechMediaTelecomNews/idUSN2053486920090820). Reuters. . Retrieved 2009-08-20.

[6] "Oracle Faces In-Depth EU Probe Over $7.4 Billion Sun Purchase" (http://www.bloomberg.com/apps/news?pid=20601085& sid=aCWYuHl5bHC8)

[7] Sun Microsystems slashing up to 3,000 jobs, 10 pct" (http://www.google.com/hostednews/ap/article/ ALeqM5giZKg-YT3GBF0lWreD262Lk77lHAD9BF2DI00), *Associated Press*, October 20, 2009

[8] Form 10-Q for SUN MICROSYSTEMS, INC. (http://biz.yahoo.com/e/091106/java10-q.html)

[9] "Oracle wins unconditional EU approval for Sun buy" (http://www.reuters.com/article/idUSTRE60K1ZN20100121). Reuters. 21 January 2010. . Retrieved 21 January 2010.

[10] "OpenSolaris devs 'ignored' by Oracle" (http://www.theregister.co.uk/2010/02/18/opensolaris_under_oracle/). 2010-02-25. . Retrieved
      2010-02-25.

[11] http://www.cuddletech.com/blog/pivot/entry.php?id=1108

[12] http://www.sun.com/service/eosl/eosl_opensolaris.html

[13] http://www.eweek.com/c/a/Linux-and-Open-Source/Oracle-Explains-Unclear-Message-About-OpenSolaris-444787/

[14] http://www.eweek.com/c/a/Linux-and-Open-Source/Oracle-Explains-Unclear-Message-About-OpenSolaris-444787/

[15] "Sun's JRuby team jumps ship to Engine Yard" (http://www.itworld.com/business/72663/suns-jruby-team-jumps-ship-engine-yard).
      2009-07-27. . Retrieved 2009-07-28.

[16] "Eric Day - Drizzling from the Rackspace Cloud" (http://oddments.org/?p=282). .

[17] "Questions and @nswers with: John Fowler" (http://www.oracle.com/profit/features/qand@.html). *Profit Magazine*. Oracle
      Corporation. . Retrieved 2010-02-15.

[18] Kelly Fiveash (2010-03-09). "Open source boss quits Sun Oracle" (http://www.theregister.co.uk/2010/03/09/
      simon_phipps_quits_sun_oracle/). *The Register*. . Retrieved 2010-02-15.

[19] http://www.oracle.com/technology/community/sun-oracle-community-continuity.html

[20] http://www.theregister.co.uk/2010/02/04/oracle_lights_out_for_project_darkstar/Article at The Register regarding Oracle shutting
      down Project Darkstar

[21] http://www.projectdarkstar.com/forum/?topic=1540.0 Project Darkstar developers announce the shutdown on the community forums

[22] Monty Widenius. "Save MySQL!" (http://www.helpmysql.org). . Retrieved 2010-01-31. "[Signer hereby asks] competition authorities
      around the world to block Oracle's acquisition of Sun unless one of the structural solutions selected by [signer] below is put in place as a
      legally binding requirement: (select at least one; all combinations are possible) MySQL must be divested to a suitable third party that can
      continue to develop it under the GPL. Oracle must commit to a linking exception for applications that use MySQL with the client libraries (for
      all programming languages), for plugins and libmysqld. MySQL itself remains licensed under the GPL. Oracle must release all past and future
      versions of MySQL (until December 2012) under the Apache Software License 2.0 or similar permissive license so that developers of
      applications and derived versions (forks) have flexibility concerning the code."

Agnews Developmental Center

Agnews Insane Asylum	
U.S. National Register of Historic Places	
U.S. Historic District	
Location:	4000 Lafayette Ave., Santa Clara, California
Coordinates:	37°23′38″N 121°57′10″W
Built/Founded:	1906
Architect:	Stocking, Leonard, State Architect; Sellon & Hennings, McDougall, George
Architectural style(s):	Mission Revival—Spanish Colonial Revival
Governing body:	State
Added to NRHP:	August 13, 1997
NRHP Reference#:	97000829

Agnews Developmental Center is a psychiatric and medical care facility, now located in San Jose, California.

In 1885, the center, originally known as "The Great Asylum for the Insane",[1] was established as a facility for the care of the mentally ill. The main structure, a red brick edifice, was located on land near Agnew's Village, which later became part of Santa Clara.

During the 1906 San Francisco earthquake the center became infamous as the site of the Santa Clara Valley's greatest loss of life resulting from the quake. The *Daily Palo Alto* reported: "The position of the people in Agnews is critical; a number of insane persons having escaped from the demolished asylum, are running at random about the country." 117 patients and staff were killed and buried in mass graves on the site. The main building and some others were irreparably damaged.

Following this disaster, Agnews was reconstructed in the Mediterranean Revival architecture styles of Mission Revival—Spanish Colonial Revival. It resembling a college campus of two-story buildings; it re-opened circa 1911 as *Agnews State Mental Hospital*. The facility was a small self-contained town, including a multitude of construction trade "shops", a farm which raised pigs and vegetable crops, a steam generating power plant for heating the buildings by steam, and even a fire department.

At the time, it boasted the largest population in the South San Francisco Bay area, and was served by its own train station which stood at the west end of Palm Drive across Lafayette Street; the station building remained until vandalism and fire precipitated its demolition in the 1990s.

In 1926, Agnews was expanded to include a second campus about two miles (3 km) to the east in San Jose.

During its heyday, the center was renowned for progressive and compassionate treatment techniques for the mentally ill.

Individuals with developmental disabilities were first admitted to a special rehabilitation program in 1965. Many programs for the mentally ill were discontinued statewide in 1972, as a result of controversial legislation promoted by then California Governor Ronald Reagan. Since then, the center has been utilized exclusively for the care and treatment of "clients" with developmental disabilities.

The original west campus was closed in 1998 as part of a plan to reduce and eventually close the center.

Re-purposing of the land

Aerial photograph of the Sun campus at Agnews

When the west campus closed, the use of the land was the subject of local controversy. In April 1997, it was announced the state would sell an 82.5-acre (33.4 ha) parcel of the campus to Sun Microsystems for use as its corporate headquarters and R&D campus. Some objected to the arranged sale of this prime public land to a profitable corporation at the peak of a local economic and real-estate boom, while others valued the presence of a prominent high-tech employer. Also at issue was the preservation of and public access to historic Agnews Developmental Center buildings. Sun arranged the restoration of four of the historic buildings (the auditorium, the clock tower, the superintendent's villa, and the administration building) and keeps some of the facilities available for public use. An outdoor exhibit open to the public displays information and photographs regarding the center and its history.

In addition to the Sun campus, the Rivermark master planned community was allocated 152 acres (62 ha) for a variety of residential, retail, public school, and open space uses.

The Agnews site was added to the National Register of Historic Places (under the name "Agnews Insane Asylum") on August 13, 1997.[2]

In Popular Media

The punk rock band Green Day recorded the music video for their song Basket Case at Agnews.

References

[1] Context Magazine, *When the Going Gets Tough...* (http://www.contextmag.com/setFrameRedirect.asp?src=/archives/200202/
Feature0WhentheGoing.asp)

[2] "National Register Information System" (http://www.nr.nps.gov/). *National Register of Historic Places*. National Park Service.
2008-04-15. .

External links

- California Department of Developmental Services (http://www.dds.cahwnet.gov/Agnews/Index.cfm)
- Article covering land re-use controversy (http://www.metroactive.com/papers/metro/04.24.97/
  agnews-bldg-9717.html)
- *Agnews Insane Asylum* (http://www.cr.nps.gov/nr/travel/santaclara/agn.htm), U.S. National Park Service
- *New Campus, New Home* (http://www.cdyn.com/videos/files/10AH00000_29_43.mp4), a video on the
  construction of the Sun Microsystems campus and preservation of the Agnews buildings
- Agnews Historical Cemetery (http://www.findagrave.com/cgi-bin/fg.cgi?page=cr&CRid=1984683) at
  Find-A-Grave

Cobalt Networks

Cobalt Networks was a maker of low-cost Linux-based servers. Founded in 1996 in Mountain View, California under the name *Cobalt Microserver*, the company pioneered easy-to-use server appliances featuring secure web user interfaces, designed for Internet service providers (ISPs) and small to medium sized businesses. Cobalt had an extremely successful IPO in December 1999 under the ticker symbol COBT, when its stock price surged from an initial value of $22 to $128.13 at market close.[1] Less than a year later, in September 2000, Sun Microsystems announced it would acquire Cobalt for $2 billion in stock, in an attempt to compete with other Linux-based server vendors. Sun completed the acquisition in December 2000. In hindsight, the timing could not have been worse for an Internet-related acquisition, as the Internet bubble started to collapse in the last quarter of 2000, accelerating through the following year. Sun's Cobalt product line saw some initial success that soon dwindled as Cobalt's core ISP market started shrinking dramatically. In December 2003, Sun retired its Cobalt products, opting at the same time to open source the underlying software and firmware.[2]

Cobalt Networks produced many different types of appliance servers. The two most popular were the *Cobalt RaQ3* and *RaQ4*. The RaQ3 had a 300 MHz AMD K6 processor while the RaQ4 ran at 400 MHz. Cobalt also made a *RaQ2* with a 200 MHz RM5231 microprocessor along with a *RaQ 550* with a 1 GHz processor, and the *Sun Cobalt RaQ XTR*.[3]

The dedicated server market was one of the largest customer markets for Cobalt servers. CobaltRacks was and is an independent dedicated server company that purchased hundreds of servers from Cobalt Networks. Many other hosting companies and ISPs purchased Cobalt Networks servers. The servers themselves were commonly referred to as *blue pizza boxes* by employees of these hosting companies because of their size, shape and color.

System administrators could operate Cobalt systems via a small LCD display and four buttons to its right in the center of the server's front panel. Operation was akin more to controlling an appliance such as a VCR rather than a typical general-purpose server.

Although the product line was canceled by Sun three years after its acquisition, Cobalt's products had lasting impact: it was the most successful web server appliance vendor of that time, and that success motivated the founding of blade server pioneer RLX Technologies (later acquired by Hewlett-Packard).[4] Cobalt's engineers were instrumental in launching Sun's current presence in the x86 market; they designed Sun's first x86-based general purpose server, the LX50, and provided engineering and marketing resources that later produced Sun's Sun Fire V60x and V65x servers.

References

[1] Shankland, Stephen (2000-04-14). "Sour market pushes Linux stocks below IPO prices" (http://news.com.com/2100-1001-239298. html?legacy=cnet). CNET News. . Retrieved 2006-11-30.

[2] Vaughan-Nichols, Steven J (2004-01-06). "Sun's Cobalt Server Software Gets Open-Source Life" (http://www.eweek.com/article2/ 0,1759,1426299,00.asp). eWeek. . Retrieved 2006-11-30.

[3] RAQ XTR press release (http://web.archive.org/web/*/http://www.cobalt.com/about/press/2001/010117.html) at the Wayback Machine.

[4] Vance, Ashlee (2003-12-18). "Sun drives the final nail in Cobalt's coffin" (http://www.theregister.co.uk/2003/12/18/ sun_drives_the_final_nail/). . Retrieved 2007-06-09.

External links

- The Cobalt open source software repository, called BlueQuartz (http://bluequartz.org/)

Elbrus (computer)

Elbrus (Russian: Эльбрус, named after Mount Elbrus) is a series of Soviet supercomputer systems developed by Lebedev Institute of Precision Mechanics and Computer Engineering (ITMiVT) since the 1970s. Since 1990s the development continued by MCST (Moscow Center of SPARC Technologies, ru:МЦСТ), a spin-off of the ITMiVT. There are other microprocessors from MCST, that are compatible with U.S.-developed SPARC architecture.

- *Elbrus 1* (1973) was the first Soviet integrated circuit computer, and the first fourth generation Soviet computer, developed by Vsevolod Burtsev. Used tag-based architecture and ALGOL as system language like the Burroughs large systems. It was used by the Defense Ministry. A side development was an update of the 1965 BESM-6 as Elbrus-1K2.
- *Elbrus 2* (1977) was a 10-processor computer, considered the first Soviet supercomputer, with superscalar RISC processors. Re-implementation of the Elbrus 1 architecture with the fast ECL chips. It was used in the space program, nuclear weapons research, and defense systems.
- *Elbrus 3* (1986) was a 16-processor computer developed by Boris Babaian. Differing completely from the architecture of both Elbrus 1 and Elbrus 2, it employed VLIW architecture.
- *Elbrus 2000* or *E2K* was a project to implement Elbrus 3 architecture as a microprocessor.
- The current SPARC-like systems (based on microprocessors MCST R-150, R-500, R-500S) have been developed from 1996 with the *Elbrus-90micro* line. The company was formed under an agreement with Sun Microsystems in 1997.
- The company reported in 1998 the development of an innovative EPIC processor dubbed *E2K* by a team under Boris Babaian.
- *Elbrus-3M*. Single-processor computer. It was used to test the new, VLIW/EPIC (Very Long Instruction Word/Explicitly Parallel Instruction Computing) type processor. This processor is based on MCST/Elbrus E2K (or Elbrus 2000) architecture. The Elbrus processor (300 MHz, power consumption < 5 W) is fabricated with 0.13 micrometre technology. It has 75 million transistors and it executes up to 23 instructions per clock cycle. Performance: 23.7 GIPS/2.4 GFLOPS (64 bits), 4.8 GFLOPS (32 bits). This processor is manufactured in Taiwan.

- *Elbrus-3M1* is the latest computer of MCST/Elbrus. It has two Elbrus processors. It can work in parallel (using high speed connections) with others Elbrus computers. So, the Elbrus-3M1 could be used to build super computers. According to test results, the peak performance of the "Elbrus-3M1" computer is in the range of 11.6 GFLOPS to 45.2 GFLOPS, depending on the data format.

Projects

- *Elbrus-3S* will be the next computer of MCST/Elbrus, projected 2009. It will have four VLIW/EPIC type Elbrus-S processors (500 MHz, 0.09 micrometre technology, system on a chip).
- *Microprocessor Elbrus-PF*, projected 2011. 65 nm technology, 8 cores VLIW/EPIC processor. With the transition to 45 nm technology, this processor will have a clock frequency of 2 GHz, and will used in servers with a performance of 8 TFLOPS. This processor will be used to build a supercomputer with PFLOPS performance.

See also

- List of Soviet computer systems

External links

- Elbrus website in Russian [1]
- Elbrus E2K [2]
- "Elbrus" processor info (russian) [3]
- "Elbrus-3M1" computer info (russian) [4]
- (I) Power Point document "Elbrus-3M1" [5]
- (II) Power Point document "Elbrus-3M1" [6]
- (I) Power Point document "Elbrus-3S" [7]
- (II) Power Point document "Elbrus-3S" [8]
- Russian microprocessors: An overview (Spanish - Espacial.org) [9]

References

[1] http://www.mcst.ru
[2] http://www.hi-tech.ournet.md/elbrus_e2k.html
[3] http://www.mcst.ru/2-3.htm
[4] http://www.mcst.ru/8-9.htm
[5] http://www.mcst.ru/doc/070711/vorobushkov.ppt
[6] http://www.mcst.ru/doc/070711/shmaev.ppt
[7] http://www.mcst.ru/doc/070711/sherstnev.ppt
[8] http://www.mcst.ru/doc/070711/nedbailo.ppt
[9] http://www.espacial.org/miscelaneas/computacion/elbrus_mcst1.htm

List of Sun Microsystems employees

These notable people work or used to work at Sun Microsystems, now a subsidiary of Oracle Corporation.

: Top · 0–9 A B C D E F G H I J K L M N O P Q R S T U V W X Y Z

A

- Brian Aker, MySQL Director of Technology

B

- Andy Bechtolsheim, Sun co-founder, systems designer and Silicon Valley investor
- Joshua Bloch, author of *Effective Java*
- Jon Bosak, chair of the original XML working group
- Jeff Bonwick, slab-allocator, vmem and ZFS
- Steve Bourne, creator of the Bourne shell
- Tim Bray, Director of Web Technologies
- David J. Brown, SUN workstation and Solaris

C

- Bryan Cantrill, of 2005 *Technology Review* "Top 35 Young Innovators"
- Alfred Chuang, co-founder of BEA Systems
- Danny Cohen, co-creator of Cohen-Sutherland line clipping algorithms, coined the computer terms "Big Endians" and "Little Endians" (Endianness)
- Danese Cooper, Open Source Diva

D

- James Duncan Davidson, creator of the Tomcat web container and the Ant build tool
- L. Peter Deutsch, founder of Aladdin Enterprises and creator of Ghostscript
- Whitfield Diffie, Chief Security Officer, co-inventor of public-key cryptography
- Robert Drost, one of *Technology Review*'s 2004 "Top 100 Young Innovators"

F

- Dan Farmer, computer security researcher
- Marc Fleury, creator of the JBoss application server
- Ned Freed, email systems researcher, co-author of several MIME RFCs

G

- Richard P. Gabriel, Lisp expert and founder of Lucid, Inc.
- John Gage, Chief Researcher and former Science Officer; first Sun salesman
- John Gilmore, co-founder of the Electronic Frontier Foundation and Cygnus Solutions
- James Gosling, co-inventor of Java; creator of NeWS networked extensible window system; author of first (proprietary) Unix Emacs implementation.
- Berny Goodheart, author of "The Magic Garden Explained: the internals of UNIX System V Release 4: an open systems design"
- Todd Greanier, software architect, author and instructor

J

- Bill Joy, Sun co-founder and architect of BSD Unix, vi editor

K

- Vinod Khosla, Sun co-founder and Silicon Valley investor

L

- Peter van der Linden, former manager of kernel group, author of numerous Java and C books

M

- Chris Malachowsky, co-founder of NVIDIA
- Craig McClanahan, creator or the Apache Struts framework and architect of Tomcat's servlet container, Catalina
- Scott McNealy, co-founder and Chairman of the Board of Sun; CEO from 1984-2006
- Larry McVoy, CEO of BitMover
- Mårten Mickos, CEO of MySQL AB from 2001 until Sun acquisition in 2008
- Jim Mitchell, Vice President and Sun Fellow
- Ian Murdock, Vice President of Developer and Community Marketing, founder of Debian

N

- Jakob Nielsen, web-design usability authority
- Peter Norvig, Director of Research Google

O

- John Ousterhout, inventor of the Tcl scripting language

P

- Greg Papadopoulos, Executive Vice President and CTO
- Radia Perlman, sometimes known as the "Mother of the Internet"
- Simon Phipps, Chief Open Source Officer
- Kim Polese, prominent dot-com era executive
- Curtis Priem, co-founder of NVIDIA

R

- George Reyes, former CFO of Google, Inc.
- David S. H. Rosenthal, early X Window System developer and original designer of the ICCCM

S

- Bob Scheifler, leader of X Window System development from 1984 to 1996
- Eric Schmidt, former Chief Technology Officer of Sun, currently CEO of Google, Inc. and co-developer of lex
- Jonathan I. Schwartz, President and CEO of Sun
- Bob Sproull, computer graphics pioneer
- Guy L. Steele, Jr., co-inventor of the Scheme programming language and member of IEEE standards committees of many programming languages
- Bert Sutherland, manager of Sun Labs, Xerox PARC, BBN Computer Science Division
- Ivan Sutherland, computer graphics pioneer

T

- Bruce Tognazzini, computer usability consultant
- Marc Tremblay, microprocessor architect and Sun's employee with the most awarded patents
- Bud Tribble, former VP of software development at NeXT, current VP of software technology at Apple

V

- Bill Vass, President and COO of Sun Microsystems Federal, Inc.

W

- Michael Widenius, original author of MySQL

Z

- Edward Zander, former President of Sun Microsystems; former CEO of Motorola

Java (programming language)

Paradigm	Object-oriented, structured, imperative
Appeared in	1995
Designed by	Sun Microsystems (now owned by Oracle Corporation)
Developer	James Gosling & Sun Microsystems
Stable release	Java Standard Edition 6 (1.6.0_22) (October 12, 2010)
Typing discipline	Static, strong, safe, nominative, manifest
Major implementations	OpenJDK, HotSpot, many others
Dialects	Generic Java, Pizza
Influenced by	Ada 83, C++, C#,[1] Delphi Object Pascal,[2] Eiffel,[3] Generic Java, Mesa,[4] Modula-3,[5] Objective-C,[6] UCSD Pascal,[7] [8] Smalltalk
Influenced	Ada 2005, BeanShell, C#, Clojure, D, ECMAScript, Groovy, J#, JavaScript, PHP, Python, Scala
OS	Cross-platform (multi-platform)
License	GNU General Public License / Java Community Process
Usual file extensions	.java, .class, .jar
Website	For Java Developers [9]
	Java Programming at Wikibooks

Java is a programming language originally developed by James Gosling at Sun Microsystems (which is now a subsidiary of Oracle Corporation) and released in 1995 as a core component of Sun Microsystems' Java platform. The language derives much of its syntax from C and C++ but has a simpler object model and fewer low-level facilities. Java applications are typically compiled to bytecode (class file) that can run on any Java Virtual Machine (JVM) regardless of computer architecture. Java is a general-purpose, concurrent, class-based, object-oriented language that is specifically designed to have as few implementation dependencies as possible. It is intended to let application developers "write once, run anywhere". Java is currently one of the most popular programming languages in use, and is widely used from application software to web applications.[10] [11]

Duke, the Java mascot

The original and reference implementation Java compilers, virtual machines, and class libraries were developed by Sun from 1995. As of May 2007, in compliance with the specifications of the Java Community Process, Sun relicensed most of its Java technologies under the GNU General Public License. Others have also developed alternative implementations of these Sun technologies, such as the GNU Compiler for Java, GNU Classpath, and Dalvik.

History

James Gosling, Mike Sheridan, and Patrick Naughton initiated the Java language project in June 1991.[12] Java was originally designed for interactive television, but it was too advanced.[13] The language was initially called *Oak* after an oak tree that stood outside Gosling's office; it went by the name *Green* later, and was later renamed *Java*, from a list of random words.[14] Gosling aimed to implement a virtual machine and a language that had a familiar C/C++ style of notation.[15]

Sun Microsystems released the first public implementation as Java 1.0 in 1995. It promised "Write Once, Run Anywhere" (WORA), providing no-cost run-times on popular platforms. Fairly secure and featuring configurable security, it allowed network- and file-access restrictions. Major web browsers soon incorporated the ability to run Java *applets* within web pages, and Java quickly became popular. With the advent of *Java 2* (released initially as J2SE 1.2 in December 1998–1999), new versions had multiple configurations built for different types of platforms. For example, *J2EE* targeted enterprise applications and the greatly stripped-down version *J2ME* for mobile applications (Mobile Java). *J2SE* designated the Standard Edition. In 2006, for marketing purposes, Sun renamed new J2 versions as *Java EE*, *Java ME*, and *Java SE*, respectively.

In 1997, Sun Microsystems approached the ISO/IEC JTC1 standards body and later the Ecma International to formalize Java, but it soon withdrew from the process.[16] Java remains a *de facto* standard, controlled through the Java Community Process.[17] At one time, Sun made most of its Java implementations available without charge, despite their proprietary software status. Sun generated revenue from Java through the selling of licenses for specialized products such as the Java Enterprise System. Sun distinguishes between its Software Development Kit (SDK) and Runtime Environment (JRE) (a subset of the SDK); the primary distinction involves the JRE's lack of the compiler, utility programs, and header files.

On November 13, 2006, Sun released much of Java as open source software under the terms of the GNU General Public License (GPL). On May 8, 2007, Sun finished the process, making all of Java's core code available under free software/open-source distribution terms, aside from a small portion of code to which Sun did not hold the copyright.[18]

Sun's vice-president Rich Green has said that Sun's ideal role with regards to Java is as an "evangelist."[19]

Following Oracle Corporation's acquisition of Sun Microsystems in 2009–2010, Oracle has described itself as the "steward of Java technology with a relentless commitment to fostering a community of participation and transparency".[20]

Principles

There were five primary goals in the creation of the Java language:[21]

1. It should be "simple, object oriented, and familiar".
2. It should be "robust and secure".
3. It should be "architecture neutral and portable".
4. It should execute with "high performance".
5. It should be "interpreted, threaded, and dynamic".

Practices

Java Platform

One characteristic of Java is portability, which means that computer programs written in the Java language must run similarly on any supported hardware/operating-system platform. This is achieved by compiling the Java language code to an intermediate representation called Java bytecode, instead of directly to platform-specific machine code. Java bytecode instructions are analogous to machine code, but are intended to be interpreted by a virtual machine (VM) written specifically for the host hardware. End-users commonly use a Java Runtime Environment (JRE) installed on their own machine for standalone Java applications, or in a Web browser for Java applets.

Standardized libraries provide a generic way to access host-specific features such as graphics, threading, and networking.

A major benefit of using bytecode is porting. However, the overhead of interpretation means that interpreted programs almost always run more slowly than programs compiled to native executables would. Just-in-Time compilers were introduced from an early stage that compile bytecodes to machine code during runtime. Over the years, this JVM built-in feature has been optimized to a point where the JVM's performance competes with natively compiled C code.

Implementations

Sun Microsystems officially licenses the Java Standard Edition platform for Linux,[22] Mac OS X,[23] and Solaris. Although in the past Sun has licensed Java to Microsoft, the license has expired and has not been renewed.[24] Through a network of third-party vendors and licensees,[25] alternative Java environments are available for these and other platforms.

Sun's trademark license for usage of the Java brand insists that all implementations be "compatible". This resulted in a legal dispute with Microsoft after Sun claimed that the Microsoft implementation did not support RMI or JNI and had added platform-specific features of their own. Sun sued in 1997, and in 2001 won a settlement of US$20 million, as well as a court order enforcing the terms of the license from Sun.[26] As a result, Microsoft no longer ships Java with Windows, and in recent versions of Windows, Internet Explorer cannot support Java applets without a third-party plugin. Sun, and others, have made available free Java run-time systems for those and other versions of Windows.

Platform-independent Java is essential to the Java EE strategy, and an even more rigorous validation is required to certify an implementation. This environment enables portable server-side applications, such as Web services, Java Servlets, and Enterprise JavaBeans, as well as with embedded systems based on OSGi, using Embedded Java environments. Through the new GlassFish project, Sun is working to create a fully functional, unified open source implementation of the Java EE technologies.

Sun also distributes a superset of the JRE called the Java Development Kit (commonly known as the JDK), which includes development tools such as the Java compiler, Javadoc, Jar, and debugger.

Performance

Programs written in Java have a reputation for being slower and requiring more memory than those written in C.[27] However, Java programs' execution speed improved significantly with the introduction of Just-in-time compilation in 1997/1998 for Java 1.1,[28] the addition of language features supporting better code analysis (such as inner classes, StringBuffer class, optional assertions, etc.), and optimizations in the Java Virtual Machine itself, such as HotSpot becoming the default for Sun's JVM in 2000.

To boost even further the speed performances that can be achieved using the Java language, Systronix made JStik,[29] a microcontroller based on the aJile Systems[30] line of embedded Java processors. In addition, the widely used ARM family of CPUs has hardware support for executing Java bytecode through its Jazelle option.

Automatic memory management

Java uses an automatic garbage collector to manage memory in the object lifecycle. The programmer determines when objects are created, and the Java runtime is responsible for recovering the memory once objects are no longer in use. Once no references to an object remain, the unreachable memory becomes eligible to be freed automatically by the garbage collector. Something similar to a memory leak may still occur if a programmer's code holds a reference to an object that is no longer needed, typically when objects that are no longer needed are stored in containers that are still in use. If methods for a nonexistent object are called, a "null pointer exception" is thrown.[31] [32]

One of the ideas behind Java's automatic memory management model is that programmers can be spared the burden of having to perform manual memory management. In some languages, memory for the creation of objects is implicitly allocated on the stack, or explicitly allocated and deallocated from the heap. In the latter case the responsibility of managing memory resides with the programmer. If the program does not deallocate an object, a memory leak occurs. If the program attempts to access or deallocate memory that has already been deallocated, the result is undefined and difficult to predict, and the program is likely to become unstable and/or crash. This can be partially remedied by the use of smart pointers, but these add overhead and complexity. Note that garbage collection does not prevent "logical" memory leaks, i.e. those where the memory is still referenced but never used.

Garbage collection may happen at any time. Ideally, it will occur when a program is idle. It is guaranteed to be triggered if there is insufficient free memory on the heap to allocate a new object; this can cause a program to stall momentarily. Explicit memory management is not possible in Java.

Java does not support C/C++ style pointer arithmetic, where object addresses and unsigned integers (usually long integers) can be used interchangeably. This allows the garbage collector to relocate referenced objects and ensures type safety and security.

As in C++ and some other object-oriented languages, variables of Java's primitive data types are not objects. Values of primitive types are either stored directly in fields (for objects) or on the stack (for methods) rather than on the heap, as commonly true for objects (but see Escape analysis). This was a conscious decision by Java's designers for performance reasons. Because of this, Java was not considered to be a pure object-oriented programming language. However, as of Java 5.0, autoboxing enables programmers to proceed as if primitive types were instances of their wrapper class.

Syntax

The syntax of Java is largely derived from C++. Unlike C++, which combines the syntax for structured, generic, and object-oriented programming, Java was built almost exclusively as an object-oriented language. All code is written inside a class, and everything is an object, with the exception of the intrinsic data types (ordinal and real numbers, boolean values, and characters), which are not classes for performance reasons.

Java suppresses several features (such as operator overloading and multiple inheritance) for *classes* in order to simplify the language and to prevent possible errors and anti-pattern design.

Java uses similar commenting methods to C++. There are three different styles of comment: a single line style marked with two slashes (//), a multiple line style opened with a slash asterisk (/*) and closed with an asterisk slash (*/), and the Javadoc commenting style opened with a slash and two asterisks (/**) and closed with an asterisk slash (*/). The Javadoc style of commenting allows the user to run the Javadoc executable to compile documentation for the program.

Example:

```
// This is an example of a single line comment using two slashes

/* This is an example of a multiple line comment using the slash and
```

```
asterisk.
   This type of comment can be used to hold a lot of information or
deactivate
   code but it is very important to remember to close the comment. */

/**
 * This is an example of a Javadoc comment; Javadoc can compile
documentation
 *  from this text.
 */
```

Examples

Hello world

The traditional Hello world program can be written in Java as:

```java
// Outputs "Hello, world!" and then exits
public class HelloWorld {
    public static void main(String[] args) {
        System.out.println("Hello, world!");
    }
}
```

To compare this to other programming languages see the list of hello world program examples.

Source files must be named after the public class they contain, appending the suffix .java, for example, HelloWorld.java. It must first be compiled into bytecode, using a Java compiler, producing a file named HelloWorld.class. Only then can it be executed, or 'launched'. The java source file may only contain one public class but can contain multiple classes with less than public access and any number of public inner classes.

A **class** that is not declared **public** may be stored in any .java file. The compiler will generate a class file for each class defined in the source file. The name of the class file is the name of the class, with *.class* appended. For class file generation, anonymous classes are treated as if their name were the concatenation of the name of their enclosing class, a $, and an integer.

The keyword **public** denotes that a method can be called from code in other classes, or that a class may be used by classes outside the class hierarchy. The class hierarchy is related to the name of the directory in which the .java file is located.

The keyword **static** in front of a method indicates a static method, which is associated only with the class and not with any specific instance of that class. Only static methods can be invoked without a reference to an object. Static methods cannot access any method variables that are not static.

The keyword **void** indicates that the main method does not return any value to the caller. If a Java program is to exit with an error code, it must call System.exit() explicitly.

The method name "main" is not a keyword in the Java language. It is simply the name of the method the Java launcher calls to pass control to the program. Java classes that run in managed environments such as applets and Enterprise JavaBean do not use or need a main() method. A java program may contain multiple classes that have main methods, which means that the VM needs to be explicitly told which class to launch from.

The main method must accept an array of **String** objects. By convention, it is referenced as **args** although any other legal identifier name can be used. Since Java 5, the main method can also use variable arguments, in the form of public static void main(String... args), allowing the main method to be invoked with an arbitrary number of String arguments. The effect of this alternate declaration is semantically identical (the args parameter is still an array of String objects), but allows an alternative syntax for creating and passing the array.

The Java launcher launches Java by loading a given class (specified on the command line or as an attribute in a JAR) and starting its public static void main(String[]) method. Stand-alone programs must declare this method explicitly. The String[] args parameter is an array of String objects containing any arguments passed to the class. The parameters to main are often passed by means of a command line.

Printing is part of a Java standard library: The **System** class defines a public static field called **out**. The out object is an instance of the PrintStream class and provides many methods for printing data to standard out, including **println(String)** which also appends a new line to the passed string.

The string "Hello, world!" is automatically converted to a String object by the compiler.

A more comprehensive example

```java
// OddEven.java
import javax.swing.JOptionPane;

public class OddEven {
    // "input" is the number that the user gives to the computer
    private int input; // a whole number("int" means integer)

    /*
     * This is the constructor method. It gets called when an object of
    the OddEven type
     * is being created.
     */
    public OddEven() {
        /*
         * Code not shown for simplicity.  In most Java programs
    constructors can initialize objects
         * with default values, or create other objects that this object
    might use to perform its
         * functions.  In some Java programs, the constructor may simply be
    an empty function if nothing
         * needs to be initialized prior to the functioning of the object.
     In this program's case, an
         * empty constructor would suffice, even if it is empty. A
    constructor must exist, however if the
         * user doesn't put one in then the compiler will create an empty
    one.
         */
    }

    // This is the main method. It gets called when this class is run
    through a Java interpreter.
    public static void main(String[] args) {
        /*
```

```
        * This line of code creates a new instance of this class
called "number" (also known as an
        * Object) and initializes it by calling the constructor.  The
next line of code calls
        * the "showDialog()" method, which brings up a prompt to ask
you for a number
        */
        OddEven number = new OddEven();
        number.showDialog();
    }


    public void showDialog() {
        /*
        * "try" makes sure nothing goes wrong. If something does,
        * the interpreter skips to "catch" to see what it should do.
        */
        try {
            /*
            * The code below brings up a JOptionPane, which is a
dialog box
            * The String returned by the "showInputDialog()" method is
 converted into
            * an integer, making the program treat it as a number
instead of a word.
            * After that, this method calls a second method,
calculate() that will
            * display either "Even" or "Odd."
            */
            input =
Integer.parseInt(JOptionPane.showInputDialog("Please Enter A Number"));
            calculate();
        } catch (NumberFormatException e) {
            /*
            * Getting in the catch block means that there was a
problem with the format of
            * the number. Probably some letters were typed in instead
of a number.
            */
            System.err.println("ERROR: Invalid input. Please type in a
numerical value.");
        }
    }

    /*
    * When this gets called, it sends a message to the interpreter.
    * The interpreter usually shows it on the command prompt (For
Windows users)
```

```
 * or the terminal (For Linux users).(Assuming it's open)
 */
private void calculate() {
    if (input % 2 == 0) {
        System.out.println("Even");
    } else {
        System.out.println("Odd");
    }
}
}
```

- The **import** statement imports the **JOptionPane** class from the **javax.swing** package.
- The **OddEven** class declares a single **private** field of type **int** named **input**. Every instance of the OddEven class has its own copy of the input field. The private declaration means that no other class can access (read or write) the input field.
- **OddEven()** is a **public** constructor. Constructors have the same name as the enclosing class they are declared in, and unlike a method, have no return type. A constructor is used to initialize an object that is a newly created instance of the class.
- The **calculate()** method is declared without the static keyword. This means that the method is invoked using a specific instance of the OddEven class. (The reference used to invoke the method is passed as an undeclared parameter of type OddEven named **this**.) The method tests the expression input % 2 == 0 using the **if** keyword to see if the remainder of dividing the input field belonging to the instance of the class by two is zero. If this expression is true, then it prints **Even**; if this expression is false it prints **Odd**. (The input field can be equivalently accessed as this.input, which explicitly uses the undeclared this parameter.)
- **OddEven number = new OddEven();** declares a local object reference variable in the main method named number. This variable can hold a reference to an object of type OddEven. The declaration initializes number by first creating an instance of the OddEven class, using the **new** keyword and the OddEven() constructor, and then assigning this instance to the variable.
- The statement **number.showDialog();** calls the calculate method. The instance of OddEven object referenced by the number local variable is used to invoke the method and passed as the undeclared this parameter to the calculate method.
- **input = Integer.parseInt(JOptionPane.showInputDialog("Please Enter A Number"));** is a statement that converts the type of **String** to the primitive data type **int** by using a utility function in the primitive wrapper class **Integer**.

Special classes

Applet

Java applets are programs that are embedded in other applications, typically in a Web page displayed in a Web browser.

```
// Hello.java
import javax.swing.JApplet;
import java.awt.Graphics;

public class Hello extends JApplet {

    @Override
```

```
public void paint(Graphics g) {
    g.drawString("Hello, world!", 65, 95);
}

}
```

The **import** statements direct the Java compiler to include the **javax.swing.JApplet** and **java.awt.Graphics** classes in the compilation. The import statement allows these classes to be referenced in the source code using the *simple class name* (i.e. JApplet) instead of the *fully qualified class name* (i.e. javax.swing.JApplet).

The Hello class **extends** (subclasses) the **JApplet** (Java Applet) class; the JApplet class provides the framework for the host application to display and control the lifecycle of the applet. The JApplet class is a JComponent (Java Graphical Component) which provides the applet with the capability to display a graphical user interface (GUI) and respond to user events.

The Hello class overrides the **paintComponent(Graphics)** method inherited from the Container superclass to provide the code to display the applet. The paintComponent() method is passed a **Graphics** object that contains the graphic context used to display the applet. The paintComponent() method calls the graphic context **drawString(String, int, int)** method to display the **"Hello, world!"** string at a pixel offset of (**65, 95**) from the upper-left corner in the applet's display.

```
<!DOCTYPE HTML PUBLIC "-//W3C//DTD HTML 4.01//EN"
"http://www.w3.org/TR/html4/strict.dtd">
<!-- Hello.html -->
<html>
  <head>
    <title>Hello World Applet</title>
  </head>
  <body>
    <applet code="Hello" width="200" height="200">
    </applet>
  </body>
</html>
```

An applet is placed in an HTML document using the **<applet>** HTML element. The applet tag has three attributes set: **code="Hello"** specifies the name of the JApplet class and **width="200" height="200"** sets the pixel width and height of the applet. Applets may also be embedded in HTML using either the object or embed element,[33] although support for these elements by Web browsers is inconsistent.[34] However, the applet tag is deprecated, so the object tag is preferred where supported.

The host application, typically a Web browser, instantiates the **Hello** applet and creates an AppletContext for the applet. Once the applet has initialized itself, it is added to the AWT display hierarchy. The paintComponent() method is called by the AWT event dispatching thread whenever the display needs the applet to draw itself.

Servlet

Java Servlet technology provides Web developers with a simple, consistent mechanism for extending the functionality of a Web server and for accessing existing business systems. Servlets are server-side Java EE components that generate responses (typically HTML pages) to requests (typically HTTP requests) from clients. A servlet can almost be thought of as an applet that runs on the server side—without a face.

```java
// Hello.java
import java.io.*;
import javax.servlet.*;

public class Hello extends GenericServlet {
    public void service(ServletRequest request, ServletResponse response)
            throws ServletException, IOException {
        response.setContentType("text/html");
        final PrintWriter pw = response.getWriter();
        pw.println("Hello, world!");
        pw.close();
    }
}
```

The **import** statements direct the Java compiler to include all of the public classes and interfaces from the **java.io** and **javax.servlet** [35] packages in the compilation.

The **Hello** class **extends** the **GenericServlet** [36] class; the GenericServlet class provides the interface for the server to forward requests to the servlet and control the servlet's lifecycle.

The Hello class overrides the **service(ServletRequest, ServletResponse)** [37] method defined by the Servlet [38] interface to provide the code for the service request handler. The service() method is passed a **ServletRequest** [39] object that contains the request from the client and a **ServletResponse** [40] object used to create the response returned to the client. The service() method declares that it **throws** the exceptions ServletException [41] and IOException if a problem prevents it from responding to the request.

The **setContentType(String)** [42] method in the response object is called to set the MIME content type of the returned data to **"text/html"**. The **getWriter()** [43] method in the response returns a **PrintWriter** object that is used to write the data that is sent to the client. The **println(String)** method is called to write the **"Hello, world!"** string to the response and then the **close()** method is called to close the print writer, which causes the data that has been written to the stream to be returned to the client.

JavaServer Pages

JavaServer Pages (JSP) are server-side Java EE components that generate responses, typically HTML pages, to HTTP requests from clients. JSPs embed Java code in an HTML page by using the special delimiters <% and %>. A JSP is compiled to a Java *servlet*, a Java application in its own right, the first time it is accessed. After that, the generated servlet creates the response.

Swing application

Swing is a graphical user interface library for the Java SE platform. It is possible to specify a different look and feel through the pluggable look and feel system of Swing. Clones of Windows, GTK+ and Motif are supplied by Sun. Apple also provides an Aqua look and feel for Mac OS X. Where prior implementations of these looks and feels may have been considered lacking, Swing in Java SE 6 addresses this problem by using more native GUI widget drawing routines of the underlying platforms.

This example Swing application creates a single window with "Hello, world!" inside:

```java
// Hello.java (Java SE 5)
import javax.swing.*;

public class Hello extends JFrame {
    public Hello() {
        super("hello");
        setDefaultCloseOperation(WindowConstants.EXIT_ON_CLOSE);
        add(new JLabel("Hello, world!"));
        pack();
    }

    public static void main(String[] args) {
        new Hello().setVisible(true);
    }
}
```

The first **import** includes all of the public classes and interfaces from the **javax.swing** package.

The **Hello** class **extends** the **JFrame** class; the JFrame class implements a window with a title bar and a close control.

The **Hello()** constructor initializes the frame by first calling the superclass constructor, passing the parameter "hello", which is used as the window's title. It then calls the **setDefaultCloseOperation(int)** method inherited from JFrame to set the default operation when the close control on the title bar is selected to **WindowConstants.EXIT_ON_CLOSE** — this causes the JFrame to be disposed of when the frame is closed (as opposed to merely hidden), which allows the JVM to exit and the program to terminate. Next, a **JLabel** is created for the string **"Hello, world!"** and the **add(Component)** method inherited from the Container superclass is called to add the label to the frame. The **pack()** method inherited from the Window superclass is called to size the window and lay out its contents.

The **main()** method is called by the JVM when the program starts. It instantiates a new **Hello** frame and causes it to be displayed by calling the **setVisible(boolean)** method inherited from the Component superclass with the boolean parameter **true**. Once the frame is displayed, exiting the main method does not cause the program to terminate because the AWT event dispatching thread remains active until all of the Swing top-level windows have been disposed.

Generics

In 2004 generics were added to the Java language, as part of J2SE 5.0. Prior to the introduction of generics, each variable declaration had to be of a specific type. For container classes, for example, this is a problem because there is no easy way to create a container that accepts only specific types of objects. Either the container operates on all subtypes of a class or interface, usually Object, or a different container class has to be created for each contained class. Generics allow compile-time type checking without having to create a large number of container classes, each containing almost identical code.

Class libraries

- Java libraries are the compiled bytecodes of source code developed by the JRE implementor to support application development in Java. Examples of these libraries are:

  - The core libraries, which include:

    - Collection libraries that implement data structures such as lists, dictionaries, trees and sets

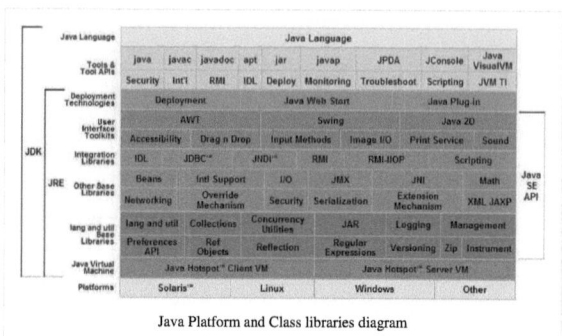

Java Platform and Class libraries diagram

  - XML Processing (Parsing, Transforming, Validating) libraries
  - Security
  - Internationalization and localization libraries

- The integration libraries, which allow the application writer to communicate with external systems. These libraries include:

  - The Java Database Connectivity (JDBC) API for database access
  - Java Naming and Directory Interface (JNDI) for lookup and discovery
  - RMI and CORBA for distributed application development
  - JMX for managing and monitoring applications

- User interface libraries, which include:

  - The (heavyweight, or native) Abstract Window Toolkit (AWT), which provides GUI components, the means for laying out those components and the means for handling events from those components
  - The (lightweight) Swing libraries, which are built on AWT but provide (non-native) implementations of the AWT widgetry
  - APIs for audio capture, processing, and playback

- A platform dependent implementation of Java Virtual Machine (JVM) that is the means by which the byte codes of the Java libraries and third party applications are executed
- Plugins, which enable applets to be run in Web browsers
- Java Web Start, which allows Java applications to be efficiently distributed to end-users across the Internet
- Licensing and documentation.

Documentation

Javadoc is a comprehensive documentation system, created by Sun Microsystems, used by many Java developers. It provides developers with an organized system for documenting their code. Whereas normal comments in Java and C are set off with /* and */, the multi-line comment tags, Javadoc comments have an extra asterisk at the beginning, so that the tags are /** and */.

Editions

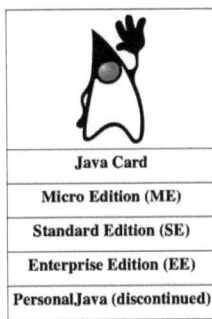

| Java Card |
| Micro Edition (ME) |
| Standard Edition (SE) |
| Enterprise Edition (EE) |
| PersonalJava (discontinued) |

Sun has defined and supports four editions of Java targeting different application environments and segmented many of its APIs so that they belong to one of the platforms. The platforms are:

- Java Card for smartcards.
- Java Platform, Micro Edition (Java ME) — targeting environments with limited resources.
- Java Platform, Standard Edition (Java SE) — targeting workstation environments.
- Java Platform, Enterprise Edition (Java EE) — targeting large distributed enterprise or Internet environments.

The classes in the Java APIs are organized into separate groups called packages. Each package contains a set of related interfaces, classes and exceptions. Refer to the separate platforms for a description of the packages available.

The set of APIs is controlled by Sun Microsystems in cooperation with others through the Java Community Process program. Companies or individuals participating in this process can influence the design and development of the APIs. This process has been a subject of controversy.

Sun also provided an edition called PersonalJava that has been superseded by later, standards-based Java ME configuration-profile pairings.

See also

- Comparison of programming languages
- Comparison of Java and C++
- Comparison of Java and C#
- JavaOne
- Javapedia
- List of Java virtual machines
- List of Java APIs
- List of JVM languages
- C#
- Java version history
- Oak

Notes

[1] Java 5.0 added several new language features (the enhanced for loop, autoboxing, varargs and annotations), after they were introduced in the similar (and competing) C# language (http://www.barrycornelius.com/papers/java5/) (http://www.levenez.com/lang/)

[2] "About Microsoft's "Delegates"" (http://java.sun.com/docs/white/delegates.html). . Retrieved 2010-01-11. "We looked very carefully at Delphi Object Pascal and built a working prototype of bound method references in order to understand their interaction with the Java programming language and its APIs. [...] Our conclusion was that bound method references are unnecessary and detrimental to the language. This decision was made in consultation with Borland International, who had previous experience with bound method references in Delphi Object Pascal."

[3] "The Java Language Environment" (http://java.sun.com/docs/white/langenv/Intro.doc1.html#943). May 1996. .

[4] "The Java Language Specification, 2nd Edition" (http://java.sun.com/docs/books/jls/second_edition/html/intro.doc.html#237601). .

[5] "The A-Z of Programming Languages: Modula-3" (http://www.computerworld.com.au/index.php/id;1422447371;pp;3;fp;4194304;fpid;1). Computerworld.com.au. . Retrieved 2010-06-09.

[6] Patrick Naughton cites Objective-C as a strong influence on the design of the Java programming language, stating that notable direct derivatives include Java interfaces (derived from Objective-C's protocol) and primitive wrapper classes. (http://cs.gmu.edu/~sean/stuff/java-objc.html)

[7] TechMetrix Research (1999). "History of Java" (http://www.fscript.org/prof/javapassport.pdf). *Java Application Servers Report*. . "The project went ahead under the name "green" and the language was based on an old model of UCSD Pascal, which makes it possible to generate interpretive code"

[8] "A Conversation with James Gosling – ACM Queue" (http://queue.acm.org/detail.cfm?id=1017013). Queue.acm.org. 2004-08-31. . Retrieved 2010-06-09.

[9] http://www.oracle.com/technetwork/java/

[10] "Programming Language Popularity" (http://www.langpop.com/). 2009. . Retrieved 2009-01-16.

[11] "TIOBE Programming Community Index" (http://www.tiobe.com/index.php/content/paperinfo/tpci/index.html). 2009. . Retrieved 2009-05-06.

[12] Byous, Jon (ca. 1998). "Java technology: The early years" (http://web.archive.org/web/20050420081440/http://java.sun.com/features/1998/05/birthday.html). *Sun Developer Network*. Sun Microsystems. Archived from the original (http://java.sun.com/features/1998/05/birthday.html) on April 20, 2005. . Retrieved 2005-04-22.

[13] "The History of Java Technology" (http://www.java.com/en/javahistory/). *Sun Developer Network*. ca. 1995. . Retrieved 2010-04-30.

[14] "Jonathan Schwartz's Blog: Different Isn't Always Better, But Better's Always Different" (http://blogs.sun.com/jonathan/entry/better_is_always_different). Blogs.sun.com. . Retrieved 2010-06-09.

[15] Heinz Kabutz, *Once Upon an Oak* (http://www.artima.com/weblogs/viewpost.jsp?thread=7555). Artima. Retrieved April 29, 2007.

[16] Java Study Group (http://www.open-std.org/JTC1/SC22/JSG/); Why Java Was – Not – Standardized Twice (http://csdl2.computer.org/comp/proceedings/hicss/2001/0981/05/09815015.pdf); What is ECMA—and why Microsoft cares (http://techupdate.zdnet.com/techupdate/stories/main/0,14179,2832719,00.html)

[17] "Java Community Process website" (http://www.jcp.org/en/home/index). Jcp.org. 2010-05-24. . Retrieved 2010-06-09.

[18] "JAVAONE: Sun – The bulk of Java is open sourced" (http://open.itworld.com/4915/070508opsjava/page_1.html). open.itworld.com. . Retrieved 2010-06-09.

[19] "Sun's Evolving Role as Java Evangelist" (http://onjava.com/pub/a/onjava/2002/04/17/evangelism.html). O'Reilly Media. .

[20] "Oracle and Java" (http://www.oracle.com/us/technologies/java/index.html). *oracle.com*. Oracle Corporation. . Retrieved 2010-08-23. "Oracle has been a leading and substantive supporter of Java since its emergence in 1995 and takes on the new role as steward of Java technology with a relentless commitment to fostering a community of participation and transparency."

[21] "1.2 Design Goals of the JavaTM Programming Language" (http://java.sun.com/docs/white/langenv/Intro.doc2.html). Java.sun.com. 1999-01-01. . Retrieved 2010-06-09.

[22] Andy Patrizio (2006). "Sun Embraces Linux With New Java License" (http://www.internetnews.com/dev-news/article.php/3606656). *Internet News*. Web Media Brands. . Retrieved 2009-09-29.

[23] "Java for Mac OS X" (http://developer.apple.com/java/). *Apple Developer Connection*. Apple. . Retrieved 2009-09-29.

[24] "Microsoft Java Virtual Machine Support" (http://www.microsoft.com/mscorp/java/default.mspx). Microsoft.com. . Retrieved 2010-06-09.

[25] "Java SE – Licensees" (http://java.sun.com/javase/licensees.jsp). Java.sun.com. 2008-08-12. . Retrieved 2010-06-09.

[26] James Niccolai (January 23, 2001). "Sun, Microsoft settle Java lawsuit" (http://www.javaworld.com/javaworld/jw-01-2001/jw-0124-iw-mssuncourt.html). *JavaWorld* (IDG). . Retrieved 2008-07-09.

[27] Jelovic, Dejan. "Why Java Will Always Be Slower than C++" (http://www.jelovic.com/articles/why_java_is_slow.htm). . Retrieved 2008-02-15.

[28] "Symantec's Just-In-Time Java Compiler To Be Integrated Into Sun JDK 1.1" (http://www.symantec.com/about/news/release/article.jsp?prid=19970407_03). .

[29] "Official JStik Website" (http://www.jstik.com/). Jstik.com. . Retrieved 2010-06-09.

[30] "aJile Systems Inc" (http://www.ajile.com/index.php?option=com_content&task=view&id=21&Itemid=28). Ajile.com. . Retrieved 2010-06-09.

[31] "NullPointerException" (http://java.sun.com/j2se/1.4.2/docs/api/java/lang/NullPointerException.html). Java.sun.com. . Retrieved 2010-06-09.

[32] "Exceptions in Java" (http://www.artima.com/designtechniques/exceptions.html). Artima.com. . Retrieved 2010-08-10.

[33] "Using applet, object and embed Tags" (http://download.oracle.com/javase/1.5.0/docs/guide/plugin/developer_guide/using_tags. html). oracle.com. . Retrieved 2010-10-14.

[34] "Deploying Applets in a Mixed-Browser Environment" (http://download.oracle.com/javase/1.5.0/docs/guide/plugin/ developer_guide/using_tags.html#mixed). oracle.com. . Retrieved 2010-10-14.

[35] http://java.sun.com/javaee/6/docs/api/javax/servlet/package-summary.html

[36] http://java.sun.com/javaee/6/docs/api/javax/servlet/GenericServlet.html

[37] http://java.sun.com/javaee/6/docs/api/javax/servlet/Servlet.html#service(javax.servlet.ServletRequest,javax.servlet. ServletResponse)

[38] http://java.sun.com/javaee/6/docs/api/javax/servlet/Servlet.html

[39] http://java.sun.com/javaee/6/docs/api/javax/servlet/ServletRequest.html

[40] http://java.sun.com/javaee/6/docs/api/javax/servlet/ServletResponse.html

[41] http://java.sun.com/javaee/6/docs/api/javax/servlet/ServletException.html

[42] http://java.sun.com/javaee/6/docs/api/javax/servlet/ServletResponse.html#setContentType(java.lang.String)

[43] http://java.sun.com/javaee/6/docs/api/javax/servlet/ServletResponse.html#getWriter()

References

- James Gosling, *A brief history of the Green project* (https://duke.dev.java.net/green/). Java.net, no date [ca. Q1/1998]. Retrieved April 29, 2007.
- James Gosling, Bill Joy, Guy Steele, and Gilad Bracha, *The Java language specification*, third edition. Addison-Wesley, 2005. ISBN 0-321-24678-0 (see also online edition of the specification (http://java.sun.com/ docs/books/jls/index.html)).
- Tim Lindholm and Frank Yellin. *The Java Virtual Machine specification*, second edition. Addison-Wesley, 1999. ISBN 0-201-43294-3 (see also online edition of the specification (http://java.sun.com/docs/books/vmspec/ 2nd-edition/html/VMSpecTOC.doc.html)).

External links

- Java: Java for End-users (http://www.java.com/)
- Oracle: Developer Resources for Java Technology (http://www.oracle.com/technetwork/java/).
- Chamber of Chartered Java Professionals International: Professionalism for Java Technology (http://www. ccjpint.org/).
- Sun Microsystems: Java Language Specification 3rd Edition (http://java.sun.com/docs/books/jls/ third_edition/html/j3TOC.html).
- Java SE 6 API Javadocs
- A Brief History of the Green Project (https://duke.dev.java.net/green/)
- Michael O'Connell: Java: The Inside Story (http://sunsite.uakom.sk/sunworldonline/swol-07-1995/ swol-07-java.html), SunWorld, July 1995.
- Patrick Naughton: Java Was Strongly Influenced by Objective-C (http://cs.gmu.edu/~sean/stuff/java-objc. html) (no date).
- David Bank: The Java Saga (http://www.wired.com/wired/archive/3.12/java.saga.html), *Wired* Issue 3.12 (December 1995).
- Shahrooz Feizabadi: A history of Java (http://ei.cs.vt.edu/~wwwbtb/book/chap1/java_hist.html) in: Marc Abrams, ed., *World Wide Web − Beyond the Basics*, Prentice Hall, 1998.
- Patrick Naughton: The Long Strange Trip to Java (http://www.blinkenlights.com/classiccmp/javaorigin. html), March 18, 1996.
- Open University (UK): M254 Java Everywhere (http://computing.open.ac.uk/m254/) (free open content documents).

- is-research GmbH: List of programming languages for a Java Virtual Machine (http://www.is-research.de/info/vmlanguages/).
- How Java's Floating-Point Hurts Everyone Everywhere (http://www.eecs.berkeley.edu/~wkahan/JAVAhurt.pdf), by W. Kahan and Joseph D. Darcy, University of California, Berkeley.

Java Research License

The **Java Research License**, or **JRL**, is a software distribution license created by Sun in an effort to simplify and relax the terms from the "research section" of the Sun Community Source License. Sun's J2SE 1.6.0, *Mustang*, is licensed under the JRL as well as many projects at Java.net [1].

Although the JRL has elements of an open source license, the terms forbid any commercial use and are thus incompatible with both the Free Software Definition and the Open Source Definition. The JRL is a research license to be used for non-commercial academic uses.

See also

- Sun Microsystems
- Java Research License – full text of the JRL

External links

- Official JRL [2]

References

[1] http://java.net
[2] http://www.java.net/jrl.csp

Java concurrency

Java is a programming language (and API) which has been designed to support concurrent programming, and all execution in the language takes place in the context of a thread. It is important for a Java programmer to understand both the power and limitations of Java threads.

In the JVM (Java Virtual Machine), objects and resources can be accessed by many separate threads; each thread has its own path of execution but can potentially access any object in the program. The programmer must ensure that threads do not interfere with each other, and that resources are properly coordinated (or "synchronized") during both read and write access. The Java language has built-in constructs to support this coordination.

The Java Language Specification does not say how the JVM designer should implement the multithreading primitives specified, because there is so much variation among the various operating systems and hardware on which the JVM is expected to run.

Monitor synchronization in Java

The key synchronization concept in Java is the monitor. Every object in a JVM has a monitor associated with it. Such monitor-based concurrency was originally introduced with the Mesa programming language.

Changes in Java 5

Java 5 incorporated many additions and clarifications to the Java concurrency model. JSR 133 provided support for well-defined atomic operations in a multithreaded/multiprocessor environment, opening the door to JSR 166, a large battery of concurrent programming APIs.

See also

- Monitor (synchronization)
- Concurrency (computer science)
- Concurrency pattern
- Doug Lea
- Thread (computer science)

References

- Goetz, Brian; Joshua Bloch, Joseph Bowbeer, Doug Lea, David Holmes, Tim Peierls (2006). *Java Concurrency in Practice*. Addison Wesley. ISBN 0-321-34960-1.
- Lea, Doug (1999). *Concurrent Programming in Java: Design Principles and Patterns*. Addison Wesley. ISBN 0-201-31009-0.

External links

- JDK 5.0 concurrency utilities [1]
- Podcast from JavaPolis - 'Concurrency Utilities in JDK 5.0 by Brian Goetz' [2]
- JavaOne 2005 - Concurrency Utilities in Practice [3]
- JavaOne 2005 - Brian Goetz - Simpler, Faster, Better: Concurrency Utilities in JDK Software Version 5.0 [4]
- Podcast from JavaPosse - Interview with Brian Goetz on Concurrency in Java 5 [5]
- William Pugh's Java Memory Model page [6]
- Java Concurrency Tutorial by Jakob Jenkov [7]
- Thread Safe Java Programming by Vadym Ustymenko [8]

References

[1] http://java.sun.com/j2se/1.5.0/docs/guide/concurrency/index.html
[2] http://www.javapolis.com/confluence/display/JP05/2006/05/23/Concurrency+Utilities+in+JDK+5.0+talk+by+Brian+Goetz
[3] http://developers.sun.com/learning/javaoneonline/2005/coreplatform/TS-3423.pdf
[4] http://developers.sun.com/learning/javaoneonline/2005/coreplatform/TS-5807.pdf
[5] http://javaposse.com/index.php?post_id=95780
[6] http://www.cs.umd.edu/~pugh/java/memoryModel/
[7] http://tutorials.jenkov.com/java-concurrency/index.html
[8] http://javatip.com/2010/07/core-java/concurrency/thread-safe-without-synchronization/

JavaOne

JavaOne is an annual conference inaugurated in 1996 by Sun Microsystems to discuss Java technologies, primarily among Java developers. JavaOne is held in San Francisco, California typically running from Sunday to Friday. Technical sessions on a variety of topics are held during the day. In the evening, Birds of a Feather (BOF) sessions are held. BOF sessions allow people to focus in on a particular aspect of Java technology.

Access to the technical sessions, keynote presentations, exhibits and BOF sessions requires a conference pass which usually costs between $1795 to $1995 USD.

In 1999, the conference played host to an event called the Hackathon, a challenge set by John Gage. Attendees were to write a program in Java for the new Palm V using the infrared port to communicate with other Palm users and register the device on the Internet.

JavaOne 2010, the first conference to be run after the acquisition of Sun by Oracle Corporation, was held September 19-23, concurrently with Oracle OpenWorld. This was the first year that the conference was not held at Moscone Center, instead hosted at several nearby hotels.

Attendees at the 2004 JavaOne conference described their vision of the future of Java on a whiteboard.

JavaOne 2011 is scheduled for October 2-6, 2011.

CommunityOne

In 2007, an associated one-day event, **CommunityOne**, was initiated, for the broader free and open-source developer community. In 2008, the second annual CommunityOne event was held on May 5.

In 2009, CommunityOne expanded to New York City (CommunityOne East, March 18-19) and to Oslo, Norway (CommunityOne North, April 15). The third annual CommunityOne in San Francisco took place from June 1-3, 2009, at Moscone Center.

Tracks included:

- **Cloud Platforms** – Development and deployment in the cloud.
- **Social and Collaborative Platforms** – Social networks and Web 2.0 trends.
- **RIAs and Scripting** – Rich Internet Applications, scripting and tools.
- **Web Platforms** – Dynamic languages, databases, and Web servers.
- **Server-side Platforms** – SOA, tools, application servers, and databases.

- **Mobile Development** – Mobile platforms, devices, tools and application development.
- **Operating Systems and Infrastructure** – Performance, virtualization, and native development.
- **Free and Open** – Open-source projects, business models, and trends.

CommunityOne was discontinued after the acquisition of Sun by Oracle.

Show device

Each year at the conference there is a hardware device highlighted, available to attendees, typically before sold to the general public or at a steep discount.

- 1998: Java ring
- 1999: Palm V[1]
- 2000
- 2001
- 2002: Sharp Zaurus[2]
- 2003
- 2004: Homepod, a wireless MP3 device from Gloolabs[3]
- 2005
- 2006: SavaJe Jasper S20 phone
- 2007: RS Media programmable robot
- 2008: Sentilla Perk Kit, Pulse Smartpen, Sony Ericsson K850i
- 2009: HTC Diamond with JavaFX preinstalled?

Java ring

References

[1] JavaOne's Palm-sized winner (http://www.javaworld.com/jw-08-1999/jw-08-javaone-palm.html)

[2] JavaOne - Day3 - Wireless World (http://www.oreillynet.com/onjava/blog/2002/03/javaone_day3_wireless_world.html)

[3] And the JavaOne 2004 "Official Show Device" is... (http://www.javalobby.org/nl/archive/jlnews_20040622o.html)

External links

- JavaOne Web Site (http://www.oracle.com/us/javaonedevelop/)
- Moscone Center (http://www.moscone.com/)
- JavaOne 2009 Blog Coverage (http://canoo.com/blog/category/javaone/)

K virtual machine

The **K virtual machine** (KVM) is a virtual machine developed by Sun Microsystems, derived from the Java virtual machine specification. The KVM was written from scratch in C. It is designed for small devices and has a small memory footprint. It supports a subset of the features of the higher end JVM. For example, a KVM may not support floating-point operations and object finalization. The CLDC specifies use of the KVM. The 'K' in KVM stands for kilobyte, signifying that the KVM runs in kilobytes of memory as opposed to megabytes.[1]

References

[1] "The K virtual machine (KVM)" (http://java.sun.com/products/cldc/wp/). .

OMS Video

OMS Video is an open, royalty-free video compression specification currently under development by Sun Microsystems's Open Media Commons as part of the Open Media Stack. It defines a video decoder and the associated bitstream syntax.[1] It is intended for delivery, storage and playback of video streams.

It was announced on April 11, 2008. The latest version of OMS Video Specification is 0.91, released on June 9, 2009.[1]

OMS Video design

OMS Video is based on an updated version of the H.261 codec as some of the patents on it have now expired.[2] Vorbis is currently planned for use as the audio codec.[3]

References

[1] "Open Media Stack Video Specifications" (http://www.openmediacommons.org/collateral/OMS-video-specs.html). Open Media Commons. 2009-06-09. . Retrieved 2009-08-30.
[2] Nathan Willis (2008-08-22). "Sun's OMS Video codec project is a means to an end" (http://linux.com/archive/feature/145347). Linux.com. . Retrieved 2009-08-30.
[3] Robert Glidden (2008-04-11). "OMS Video, A Project of Sun's Open Media Commons Initiative" (http://blogs.sun.com/ openmediacommons/entry/oms_video_a_project_of). . Retrieved 2009-08-30.

External links

- announcement of OMS Video (http://blogs.sun.com/openmediacommons/entry/oms_video_a_project_of)
- Sun ponders video codec technology - InfoWorld (http://www.infoworld.com/article/08/04/11/ Sun-ponders-video-codec-technology_1.html)
- OpenMediaCommons.org official homepage (http://www.openmediacommons.org/)

See also

- H.261
- Vorbis
- Video compression
- Open Media Commons
- Dirac (codec)
- Theora
- Codec
- Open source codecs and containers

Oak (programming language)

Oak was a programming language created by James Gosling in 1991, initially for Sun Microsystems set-top box project. The language later evolved to become Java.

The name *Oak* was used by Gosling after an oak tree that stood outside his office.

History

In 1991, Sun Microsystems was attempting to develop a new technology for programming next generation smart appliances, which Sun expected to be a major new opportunity.

The team originally considered using C++, but rejected the idea for several reasons (see Java history).

Initially, Gosling attempted to modify and extend C++ but soon abandoned that in favor of creating a new platform called *Green* and an entirely new language, which he called **Oak**, after the tree that stood just outside his office[1].

By the summer of 1992, they were able to demonstrate portions of the new platform including the Green OS, the Oak language, the libraries, and the hardware. Their first attempt, demonstrated on September 3, 1992, focused on building a PDA device named *Star7*[star7] which had a graphical interface and a smart agent called "Duke" to assist the user.

Oak was renamed *Java* in 1994 after a trademark search revealed that *Oak* was used by Oak Technology[2]. Java 1.0 was finally shipped in 1996[3].

Differences with Java

Oak was the basis for what Java 1.0 became later, but there were also some differences[4] [5] : Several concepts were planned in the Oak specification but remained not implemented in the original language because of time constraints:

- unsigned primitive types turned out never to be implemented in Java[6].
- The *enum* keyword for enumerated types was implemented in Java for Java 5.0.
- The assert keyword was implemented in Java for Java 1.4[7]

Other concepts were different than, or improved later, for Java[4] :

- As stated in the Oak specification, integer variable types did not affect their storage allocation. For example byte or short values were stored on 4 bytes of memory. This changed in Java 1.4.
- abstract methods were defined as in C++.
- The package private access level did not exist in Oak. Classes with no access modifier were considered private.

And finally some concepts were later scraped out:

- All exceptions were unchecked.
- It was possible by the *unprotect* keyword to write code that would not signal asynchronous exceptions.

- There was some support for Design by Contract[8] : Oak had assertions whereby Class variable could be constrained and the constraints were enforced at entry and exit of every public and protected method of the class. Methods could also have their own pre-conditions and post-conditions, which were inherited but not redefinable in a subclass[9] [4] .

See also

- Java (programming language)
- Java version history

References

[1] Jon Byous (2003-03-12). "Java Technology: An early history" (http://gcc.uni-paderborn.de/www/WI/WI2/wi2_lit.nsf/ 64ae864837b22662c12573e70058bbb4/abf8d70f07c12eb3c1256de900638899/$FILE/Java Technology - An early history.pdf). Sun Microsystems. . Retrieved 2009-08-02. *"Gosling called the new language "Oak", after the tree outside his window"*

[2] Kieron Murphy (1996-04-10). "So why did they decide to call it Java?" (http://www.javaworld.com/javaworld/jw-10-1996/ jw-10-javaname.html). javaworld.com. . Retrieved 2009-08-03. *"The lawyers had told us that we couldn't use the name 'OAK' because [it was already trademarked by] Oak Technologies," said Frank Yellin, a senior engineer at Sun. "So a brainstorming session was held to come up with ideas for a new name"*

[3] Jonathan I. Schwartz (2007-08-30). "Different Isn't Always Better, But Better's Always Different" (http://blogs.sun.com/jonathan/entry/ better_is_always_different). . Retrieved 2009-08-02.

[4] Heinz Kabutz (2003-07-15). "Once Upon an Oak ..." (http://www.artima.com/weblogs/viewpost.jsp?thread=7555). artima.com. . Retrieved 2009-08-02.

[5] "Oak language specification" (https://duke.dev.java.net/green/OakSpec0.2.ps). Sun Microsystems. . Retrieved 2009-08-02.

[6] "Java and unsigned int, unsigned short, unsigned byte, unsigned long, etc. (Or rather, the lack thereof)" (http://www.darksleep.com/player/ JavaAndUnsignedTypes.html). . Retrieved 2009-08-02.

[7] "A Simple Assertion Facility For the Java Programming Language" (http://java.sun.com/docs/books/jls/assert-spec.html). Sun Microsystems. . Retrieved 2009-08-02.

[8] Johannes Rieken (2007-04-24). "Design by Contract for Java - Revised" (http://modernjass.sourceforge.net/docs/ mastersthesis-johannes_rieken.pdf). . Retrieved 2010-10-02.

[9] "Support For 'Design by Contract', beyond "a simple assertion facility"" (http://bugs.sun.com/view_bug.do?bug_id=4449383). Sun Microsystems. . Retrieved 2010-10-02.

External links

- Oak language specification (https://duke.dev.java.net/green/OakSpec0.2.ps)
- Alternative site for Oak language specification (http://www.me.umn.edu/~shivane/blogs/cafefeed/resources/ 14-jun-2007/OakSpec0.2.zip)
- Java early history (https://duke.dev.java.net/green/)

Open Media Commons

The **Open Media Commons**, sometimes referred to as the **Open Media Commons initiative**, is a computer industry group whose goal is to "develop open, royalty-free digital rights management and codec solutions". One of their largest supporters is Sun Microsystems, who released their internal digital rights management (DRM) project, Project DReaM, as part of the Open Media Commons initiative on 22 August 2005.

Project DReaM one of several project organized through the Open Media Commons initiative:

- **DRM-OPERA:** An interoperable DRM architecture that is not dependent upon a specific hardware set or operating system.
- **Java Stream Assembly:** Java-based server software that allows for distribution of video over a network.
- **Sun Streaming Server (SSS):** Serves standards-compliant video and audio media over an IP-based network. Generally, SSS serves MPEG-4 video media. It also supports Apple Computer's QuickTime.
- **OMS Video:** a royalty-free codec loosely based on the H.261 with new tools & optimizations.[1]

References

[1] OMS Video, A Project of Sun's Open Media Commons Initiative : Open Media Commons (http://blogs.sun.com/openmediacommons/
    entry/oms_video_a_project_of)

External links

- OpenMediaCommons.org official homepage (http://www.openmediacommons.org/)

Open Source University Meetup

The **Open Source University Meet-Up** is a student developer organization sponsored by Sun Microsystems that educates its members about open-source technologies through technical demonstrations, access to web courses, and discounts on Sun Certification.[1]

History

Sun started the Open Source University Meet-Up as part of its program to help connect students in computer science to its technologies. Typically lead by a campus ambassador or on-campus volunteer, Open Source University Meet-Ups exist in many countries.[2]

Purpose

The Open Source University Meet-Up is a place for Sun to connect student developers to Sun's wide array of open source software platforms, following Sun's initiatives to open-source all of its software technologies. As a whole it also helps give software developers, students, and other interested people an opportunity to learn more about open source software.[3]

See also

MSDN Academic Alliance

References

[1] Open Source University Meet-Up (OSUM) (http://developers.sun.com/students/osum/index.jsp)

[2] Campus Ambassadors Map (http://developers.sun.com/students/osum/index.jsp)

[3] About OSUM (http://www.iowaosum.com/about)

External links

- Official Homepage (http://developers.sun.com/students/osum/index.jsp)
- OSUM Network (http://osum.sun.com)
- http://www.uleth.ca/notice/display.html?b=302&s=10721
- http://www.iowaosum.com

Pixo

Pixo was a company that developed infrastructure for wireless systems. Paul Mercer left Apple in 1994 to found Pixo. The company developed a system software toolkit in C++ which was later adopted by Apple for use in the iPod. Apple continues to use Pixo OS technology in currently shipping models. The use of the Pixo OS in the iPod was never formally announced, although the first-generation iPod's "About iPod" display includes a mention of Pixo, and a Connectix biography of their VP of engineering Mike Neil mentions his role as "lead architect on the Pixo OS that is used in ... the Apple iPod".[1] Apple acquired the Pixo OS shortly after shipping the iPod and removed mention of Pixo from the "About iPod" display with a firmware update to the first-generation iPod. In 2003 Sun Microsystems bought Pixo Inc.

On April 9, 2007, Apple CEO Steve Jobs announced the shipment of its 100 millionth iPod,[2] making the Pixo OS one of the most widely used embedded operating systems.

The Pixo application framework is written in the C++ programming language.[3]

References

[1] About Connectix (at Internet Archive) (http://web.archive.org/web/20030806065941/http://www.connectix.com/about/bios.html)

[2] http://www.apple.com/pr/library/2007/04/09ipod.html

[3] List of C++ applications (http://www.research.att.com/~bs/applications.html), maintained by C++ creator Bjarne Stroustrup

External links

- Pixo.com website since 1996 (http://web.archive.org/web/*/http://www.pixo.com) (at Internet Archive)
- Capabilities and features of the Pixo OS Platform 2.1 (http://web.archive.org/web/20010815050140/pixo.com/products/products001.htm)
- Sun Press Release announcing completion of acquisition (http://web.archive.org/web/20070228031939rn_1/www.sun.com/smi/Press/sunflash/2003-07/sunflash.20030717.1.xml) (archive copy at the Internet Archive)
- SF Chronicle article on Pixo's involvement in Apple's iPod (http://www.sfgate.com/cgi-bin/article.cgi?file=/chronicle/archive/2004/08/16/BUGTG878AR1.DTL&type=printable)
- Bill Mogridge video interview of Paul Mercers involvement in the design of the iPod (http://www.designinginteractions.com/interviews/PaulMercer)
- Interview with Paul Mercer and bio of his work (http://www.nytimes.com/2006/02/27/technology/27mercer.html?ei=5088&en=7ca4508916893a7f&ex=1298696400&pagewanted=all)

Project DReaM

Project DReaM is a Sun Microsystems project whose aim is to produce an "interoperable DRM architecture implementing standardized interfaces and processes for the interoperability of DRM systems".[1] DReaM is an acronym that stands for "DRM everywhere/available". Sun's primary goal in creating Project DReaM is to release an industry standard and royalty-free digital rights management standard.

There are several key characteristics of Project DReaM that make it unique:[2]

- **Network identity focused:** Project DReaM approaches DRM (and CAS) from a network identity management focused perspective, rather than simply a device-centric approach.
- **Interoperability:** Project DReaM uses an open approach and fully specifies everything necessary to build heterogeneous, interoperable, vendor neutral implementations.
- **Not another security through obscurity approach:** Project DReaM's architecture does not follow the traditional model of security through obscurity which must maintain a closed source code base in order to operate securely.
- **Royalty-free design model:** Project DReaM is designed to be royalty free, allowing developers to avoid encumbered technology that carries onerous licensing costs. In addition to employing CDDL licensing terms, Project DReaM will rely upon other models for assuring royalty free usage such as using a Patent Commons approach.

On 22 August 2005, Sun announced that it was opening up Project DReaM as part of their Open Media Commons initiative.[1] It has been released under the Common Development and Distribution License (CDDL).

See also

- Open Media Commons

References

[1] Sun Microsystems President Jonathan Schwartz Shares Project DReaM (http://www.sun.com/smi/Press/sunflash/2005-08/sunflash. 20050822.2.html)
[2] dream: (https://dream.dev.java.net)

External links

- OpenMediaCommons.org (http://www.openmediacommons.org/)
- Project DReaM press release (http://www.sun.com/smi/Press/sunflash/2005-08/sunflash.20050822.2.html)
- https://dream.dev.java.net/

Proximity communication

Proximity communication is a Sun microsystems technology of wireless chip-to-chip communications. Partly by Robert Drost and Ivan Sutherland. Research done as part of High Productivity Computing Systems DARPA project.

Proximity communication replaces wires by capacitive coupling, promises significant increase in communications speed between chips in an electronic system, among other benefits. Partially funded by a $50 million award from the Defense Advanced Research Projects Agency.

Comparing traditional area ball bonding, proximity communication has one order smaller scale, so it can be two order densier (in terms of connection number/pin number) than ball bonding. This technique require very good alignment between chips and very small gaps between tx and rx parts (2-3 micrometers), which can be destroyed by thermal expansion, vibration, dust, etc.

Chip transmitter consists (according to presentation slide) of big 32x32 array of very small Tx micropads, 4x4 array of bigger Rx micropads (four times bigger than tx micropad), and two linear arrays of 14 X vernier and 14 Y vernier.

Proximity communication can be used with 3D packing on chips in Multi-Chip Module, allowing to connect several MCM without sockets and wires.

Speed was up to 1.35 Gbps/channel in tests of 16 channel systems. BER $< 10^{-12}$. Static power is 3.6 mW/channel, dynamic power is 3.9 pJ/bit

Current status of the project is unknown.

External links

- Book: Ron Ho, Robert Drost, Coupled Data Communication Techniques for High-Performance and Low-Power Computing [1], Springer, 2010.
- Press release [2]
- Slides by Robert J. Drost [3]
- List of Drost patents in Sun, most of which is about Proximity communication [4]

References

[1] http://www.amazon.com/Communication-Techniques-High-Performance-Low-Power-Integrated/dp/1441965874/
[2] http://research.sun.com/spotlight/2004-09-20.feature-proximity.html
[3] http://research.sun.com/sunlabsday/docs.2004/talks/1.02_Drost.pdf
[4] http://research.sun.com/people/drost/

SUN workstation

The original Stanford University Network **SUN workstation** was designed to be a low cost ($10,000) personal workstation for computer aided logic design work to replace SAIL terminals. The design goal was to create a 3M computer: a 1 MIPS processor, 1 Megabyte of memory and a 1 Megapixel Raster scan Bit-map graphics display. (The $10,000 price point was the fourth "M" — a "Megapenny"). Ethernet was included. The initial workstation was designed by Ralph Gorin and then given to Andy Bechtolsheim to create a finished design.

"The SUN workstation is a modular personal computer system designed for use in an Ethernet-type local network. A SUN workstation provides a single user with significant local computing power, a high resolution graphical display, graphical input, and network communication [Bechtolsheim]. The SUN station capabilities can be realized at a cost of approximately $10,000 per station, using commercially available VLSI components."[1]

Eventually ten SUN workstations were built in the 1981–1982 time frame. After the initial ten, Stanford declined to build any more. Andy Bechtolsheim then went out to shop the hardware design around. Many minicomputer vendors licensed the design. Many other products were based on Andy's CPU design including early Cisco routers and Imagen raster based print engines. Vinod Khosla, a fellow graduate of Stanford who was an early employee at Daisy Systems Corporation convinced Bechtolsheim along with Scott McNealy to found Sun Microsystems in order to build the Sun1/100 workstation.

The SUN workstation was made possible by the convergence of 3 technologies: VLSI, Multibus and ECAD.

VLSI (Very Large Scale Integration) in semiconductor chips finally allowed for a high level of hardware functionality to be included in a single chip. The VLSI chips included the Motorola 68000 CPU, a parallel port controller and a serial port controller.

The Multibus computer interface allowed circuit boards made by different vendors to be integrated in to a single system. This allowed the Stanford 3M design to leverage off existing Multibus circuit boards such as the Chrislin CI-8086 128 and 512 KB memory expansion boards.

ECAD (Electronic Computer Assisted Design) was a critical development for the design of the SUN workstation. It allowed integration of the VLSI subsystems along with other sub systems into a single design in software with minimal hardware "bread boarding". This allowed larger systems of greater complexity to be designed by a small group of people. The ECAD software was an offshoot of a project to design processors tailored to specific computer languages, called the S-1 processor:

"The S-1 design system was constructed to support the development of the S-1 processor. The S-1 design system consists of:

SCALD (Structured Computer Aided Logic Design) System — a hierarchically structured logic design system.

SUDS (Stanford University Drawing System) — a graphics system, used to edit, input, and output to/from SCALD.

A timing verifier — based on SCALD and designed to analyze and verify timing specifications and constraints in a digital system.

The physical design system — consists of both placement tools (chip placement) and wirewrap technology tools."[2]

References

[1] A. Bechtolsheim and F. Baskett, "A Low-cost Raster-graphics Terminal", *Proceedings SIGGRAPH 80*, July, 1980.

[2] Research in VLSI Systems Design and Architecture March 1981 (ftp://reports.stanford.edu/pub/cstr/reports/csl/tr/81/201/CSL-TR-81-201.pdf)

Jonathan I. Schwartz

Jonathan I. Schwartz	
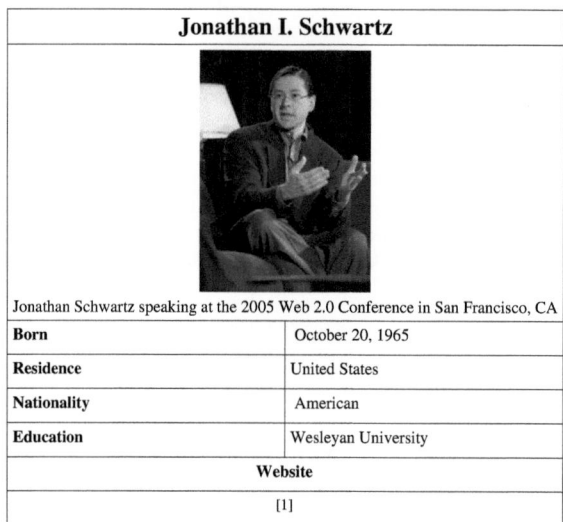	
Jonathan Schwartz speaking at the 2005 Web 2.0 Conference in San Francisco, CA	
Born	October 20, 1965
Residence	United States
Nationality	American
Education	Wesleyan University
Website	
[1]	

Jonathan Ian Schwartz (born 20 October 1965) is the co-founder and CEO of Picture of Health[2] . Up to the acquisition by Oracle he was President and CEO of Sun Microsystems.

Background

Schwartz attended Bethesda-Chevy Chase High School in Bethesda, Maryland, and graduated in 1983. He spent freshman year of college at Carnegie Mellon University in 1983-1984, and then transferred to Wesleyan University, where he studied economics and mathematics.

He is "one quarter (Asian) Indian, one quarter Welsh (on his Mother's side), one quarter Hungarian, and one quarter Russian (Father's side)."[3]

Career

Schwartz started his career in 1987 at McKinsey & Company in New York City. During that same year, Schwartz was riding on the Amtrak *Colonial* train that crashed in Chase, Maryland. According to him, the incident had a profound impact on his life.[3] In 1989, Schwartz left McKinsey and moved to Chevy Chase, Maryland, where he was a co-founder of Lighthouse Design. In the early 1990s, Lighthouse Design moved to San Mateo, California. Eventually, Schwartz became chief executive officer of Lighthouse.

In 1996, Lighthouse Design was acquired by Sun Microsystems.[4] Schwartz became the director of product marketing for JavaSoft in 1997 and then transitioned through a series of 5 vice president positions. In 2004, Schwartz was promoted to president and chief operating officer of Sun.[5] He eventually replaced Scott McNealy as

CEO.

As CEO of Sun

While CEO of Sun Microsystems in 2008, Schwartz earned a total compensation of $11,085,826, which included a base salary of $1,000,000, a cash bonus of $1,043,000, stocks granted of $4,399,460, and options granted of $4,585,000.[6] He finalized the sale of Sun Microsystems a couple of months after his payout, when he signed an agreement for the sale of the company to Oracle Corporation on April 20, 2009.[7]

As CEO of Sun, Schwartz was known as one of the few Fortune 500 CEO bloggers, and is recognized for his efforts to bring greater transparency into the corporate world. He had a public exchange with SEC Chairman Christopher Cox about the use of websites and blogs[8] to meet Regulation Fair Disclosure.[9]

Post-Sun

On February 4, 2010, Schwartz resigned from his post as CEO of Sun. His resignation was a haiku on Twitter that read as follows: "Financial crisis/Stalled too many customers/CEO no more."[10] [11]

On August 12, 2010, Schwartz was named to Taleo's board of directors, on September 9, 2010 he announced founding a new company, Picture of Health[12] .

Ideology and controversy

Schwartz regularly promotes his view that the Information Age has given way to a "Participation Age," in which people create news, ideas, and entertainment, as well as consuming them. Schwartz also speaks about the networks as a social utility—comparable to electricity or railroads—that creates an opportunity to drive social, economic and political progress.[13] [14]

References

[1] http://jonathanischwartz.wordpress.com/
[2] Who we are, Picture of Health (http://www.pictureofhealth.com/people).
[3] Five Things, Jonathan's Blog (http://blogs.sun.com/jonathan/entry/five_things_about_myself).
[4] Kalin, Sari (June 1996). " PC Expo: Sun buys object developer (http://sunsite.uakom.sk/sunworldonline/swol-06-1996/swol-06-lighthouse.html)". Accessed on August 25, 2005.
[5] Forbes.com profile for Jonathan Schwartz (http://www.forbes.com/finance/mktguideapps/personinfo/FromPersonIdPersonTearsheet.jhtml?passedPersonId=902035). Accessed on September 25, 2007.
[6] 2008 CEO Compensation for Jonathan I. Schwartz (http://www.equilar.com/CEO_Compensation/Sun_Microsystems_Jonathan_I._Schwartz.php), Equilar.com
[7] http://www.sun.com/third-party/global/oracle/Sun Microsystems and Oracle Corporation joint announcement
[8] One Small Step for the Blogosphere (http://blogs.sun.com/jonathan/entry/one_small_step_for_the)
[9] The Internet and Regulation FD (http://blogs.sun.com/jonathan/entry/regfd_and_the_odf_tidal)
[10] Resignation haiku on Twitter (http://twitter.com/OpenJonathan/status/8620937722)
[11] Sun's Chief Executive Tweets His Resignation (http://bits.blogs.nytimes.com/2010/02/04/suns-chief-executive-tweets-his-resignation/)
[12] A Picture Emerges (http://jonathanischwartz.wordpress.com/2010/09/09/pictoh/). Accessed on September 12, 2010.
[13] Sun Microsystems and Emerging Markets (http://sunfeedroom.sun.com/ifr_main.jsp?nsid=c330dbd88:11a4fc3ad89:-14d0&rf=sv&fr_story=FRsupt215040&st=1212520806980&mp=FLV&cpf=false&fr=060308_032007720_330dbd88x11a4fc3ad89xw14cf&rdm=670104.7802007153)
[14] Video Highlights from the 49th Annual McKinsey Awards (http://discussionleader.hbsp.com/hbreditors/2008/05/video_highlights_from_the_49th.html)

Articles

- Markets set free by open source (http://www.ft.com/cms/s/0/5eb9e272-82c7-11dd-a019-000077b07658. html?nclick_check=1) - Financial Times.com September 16, 2008 - Article discusses how the internet and open source allow people to participate directly in broadening economic opportunity, speeding social progress and driving market efficiency.
- Sun's 'Open'-Door Policy (http://www.eweek.com/c/a/Linux-and-Open-Source/Suns-OpenDoor-Policy/) - eWeek March 15, 2008 - Article discusses how the company is leveraging open source to make new enterprise inroads.
- The 'Warrior' Within Jonathan Schwartz (http://www.businessweek.com/technology/content/oct2007/ tc2007104_507418.htm) - Article discusses Schwartz' personal history and rise, accessed January 22, 2008
- Sun CEO Emerges From McNealy's Shadow. (http://www.sfgate.com/cgi-bin/article.cgi?f=/c/a/2006/12/ 15/BUGPDMQ1T956.DTL) - San Francisco Chronicle. December 15, 2006. After 7 months as Sun's top executive, Schwartz says the company is expanding its business.
- Blogger in Chief (http://money.cnn.com/magazines/fortune/fortune_archive/2006/11/13/8393166/index. htm) - Fortune. October 30, 2006. Jonathan Schwartz discusses his communication priorities as Sun's CEO and the importance of his blog.
- Sun Promotes Alternate View (http://www.techworld.com/opsys/news/index.cfm?NewsID=3459) - Techworld.com. April 11, 2005. Article where Schwartz felt the GPL was being used "as a tool allowing United States businesses to pillage developing countries of their intellectual property."
- Good Artists Copy, Great Artists Steal (http://jonathanischwartz.wordpress.com/2010/03/09/ good-artists-copy-great-artists-steal/) - jonathanischwartz.wordpress.com. March 9, 2010. Schwartz discusses how patent and litigation work. How and why companies maintain huge patent portfolios as a defense and also to extract royalty in case of IP misuse.

External links

- What I Couldn't Say... (http://jonathanischwartz.wordpress.com/) - Schwartz blog on things he couldn't say as Sun CEO.
- Schwartz's Twitter feed (http://twitter.com/openjonathan)
- Sun Microsystems Executive Perspectives (http://www.sun.com/aboutsun/executives/)
- Sun Microsystems Official Jonathan I. Schwartz bio (http://www.sun.com/aboutsun/executives/schwartz/bio. jsp)
- Schwartz's blog at Sun (http://blogs.sun.com/jonathan/)

Starfire video prototype

Starfire was a Sun Microsystems promotional video filmed in 1994, demonstrating Bruce Tognazzini's ideas for a 21st-century computer user interface. Inspired in part by Apple Computer's Knowledge Navigator film from 1987, Tognazzini and his team at SunSoft sought to create a more realistic look at how computer technology and interfaces would improve. The project drew together the talents of more than 100 engineers, designers, futurists, and filmmakers in an effort to both predict and guide the future of computing.

The film is set in the year 2004 and features a protagonist interacting by voice, mouse, and stylus with a 5-foot-wide computer screen (1.5 m) . The story concerns an executive at an auto-maker who must make a compelling presentation for her design.

The video predicted the rise of a new technology that would become known as the World Wide Web (board room scene).

Popular Science Magazine reported, in March 2009, that Microsoft had just produced a new video showing life in the year 2019: "The 2019 Microsoft details with this video is almost identical to the 2004 predicted in this video produced by Sun Microsystems in 1992."

In addition to the film, the project also produced:

- Tog on Software Design, which not only covers the film in intimate detail, but lays out several more equally thought-provoking scenarios, even if they were not enshrined in celluloid.
- Starfire, the Paper, published in the CHI Proceedings, outlining the rules followed in attempting to build a scientifically legitimate video prototype, as opposed to simply confabulating a fanciful, but non-implementable, vision.

The film was released as the Starfire video, in NTSC format, and later made available as part of a collection of human-computer interaction videos.

See also

Microsoft Surface - It uses similar technology such as multi touch screen.

External links

- A collection of human-computer interaction videos [1].
- Bruce Tognazzini's homepage about Starfire [2], includes the full original video.
- "Future Forward" [3] — a review of Starfire in Wired Magazine issue
- Popular Science Article on Starfire vs. Microsoft3.09 — Street Cred section [4] — author: Will Kreth.

References

[1] http://www.idemployee.id.tue.nl/g.w.m.rauterberg/movies/
[2] http://www.asktog.com/starfire/starfireHome.html
[3] http://www.wired.com/wired/archive/3.09/streetcred.html?pg=19
[4] http://www.popsci.com/scitech/article/2009-03/future-isn't-what-it-used-be

Storage Technology Corporation

Type	Subsidiary of Oracle Corporation
Industry	Computer hardware, software
Founded	1969
Headquarters	Louisville, Colorado
Key people	Patrick J. Martin, Chairman, President & CEO Eula Adams, Vice President, Global Services Jon Benson, Vice President and General Manager, Automated Tape Solutions Pierre Cousin, Corporate Vice President, Research, Development and Engineering Nigel Dessau, Vice President and Chief Marketing Officer Angel Garcia, Corporate Vice President, International Operations Roger Gaston, Corporate Vice President, Human Resources Robert Kocol,Corporate Vice President and Chief Financial Officer Roy G. Perry, Corporate Vice President, Global Supply Chain Management Brenda Zawatski, Vice President and General Manager, Information Lifecycle Management Solutions
Products	data storage hardware and software, professional and support services
Revenue	$2.2 billion USD (2004)
Employees	~7000 (2004)
Website	[1] [1]

Storage Technology Corporation (**StorageTek** or **STK**), aka **STC** until about 1983, is a data storage technology company. Current StorageTek products focus on tape backup equipment and software to manage storage systems. New products include data retention systems, which they call information lifecycle management, or ILM. Competitors include EMC and Veritas.[2] Now a subsidiary of Sun Microsystems, Inc. and referred to as **Sun StorageTek**, StorageTek was headquartered in Louisville, Colorado, United States with manufacturing facilities in Ponce, Puerto Rico.

Brief history

StorageTek was founded in 1969 by four former IBM engineers: Jesse Awieda, Juan Rodriguez, Thomas S. Kavanagh, Zoltan Herger. Storage Technology Corporation, which officially became known as StorageTek in 1983, originally challenged IBM's dominance in tape storage, expanded to compete in the printer business for more than a dozen years. In the 1970s, StorageTek launched its Disk Products division.

Plagued by a series of missteps that drained the company's cash, including a failed attempt to develop an IBM compatible mainframe, and an optical disk product line, the company filed for Chapter 11 in 1984.

New management invested in an automated tape library system that 'picked' tapes with a robot arm and stored them in a silo-like contraption in 1987. StorageTek emerged as a dominant player in the automated tape library market.

StorageTek has acquired a number of companies, including Documation (1980), Aspen Peripherals Corporation (1989), Network Systems Corporation (1995), and Storability (2005). These and other activities allowed StorageTek to expand operations in Ponce, Puerto Rico and Toulouse, France.

On June 2, 2005, Sun Microsystems, Inc. announced it would purchase Storage Technology Corporation ("StorageTek") for US$4.1 billion in cash, or $37.00 per share. On August 31, 2005, the acquisition was completed.

On January 27, 2010, Sun Microsystems, Inc. was acquired by Oracle Corporation for US$7.4 billion, based on an agreement signed on April 20, 2009.[3]

Technology milestones for StorageTek

- 1970 - StorageTek releases its first product, the 2450/2470 tape drive.
- 1971 - StorageTek introduces the 3400 tape storage device.
- 1973 - StorageTek's disk division is founded.
- 1974 - StorageTek's first 3600 tape drive ships.
- 1975 - StorageTek ships the first 8000 Super Disk and announces the 8350 disk subsystem.
- 1978 - StorageTek develops a solid-state disk.
- 1984 - StorageTek files for Chapter 11 bankruptcy protection and focuses R&D on automated tape.
- 1986 - StorageTek develops the first cached disk.
- 1987 - StorageTek develops tape automation and emerges from Chapter 11.
- 1994 - StorageTek introduces virtual disk.
- 1998 - StorageTek introduces Flexline disk arrays.
- 2001 - StorageTek introduces virtual networking.
- 2002 - StorageTek introduces BladeStore, a disk array based on ATA disk technology.
- 2003 - StorageTek introduces the EchoView data protection appliance, a disk-based appliance that eliminates the backup window.
- 2003 - StorageTek introduces the StreamLine SL8500 modular library system.

Products

- Tape libraries: L700, L700e, L180, L5500, SL500, SL3000, SL8500
- Tape drives: StorageTek 9940, 9840C, T9840D, T10000A, T10000B
- Tape drives (rebranded): LTO, SDLT, DLT
- Disk array: ST9990, ST9985, ST6540, ST6140
- Fibre Channel, SAS, RAID and SCSI HBAs.

References

[1] http://www.oracle.com/us/products/servers-storage/storage/

[2] http://news.cnet.com/Buying-StorageTek-Suns-last-big-gamble---page-2/2100-1015_3-5729961-2.html?tag=mncol Sun buys StorageTek

[3] "Oracle Completes Acquisition of Sun" (http://finance.yahoo.com/news/Oracle-Completes-Acquisition-iw-2658323391.html?x=0&.v=1). Yahoo. 27 January 2010. . Retrieved 27 January 2010.

External links

- Oracle Sun Storage Homepage (http://www.oracle.com/us/products/servers-storage/storage/)

StorageTek tape formats

Storage Technology Corporation, or **StorageTek**, has created several magnetic tape data storage **formats**. These are commonly used with large computer systems, typically in conjunction with a robotic tape library. The most recent format is the T10000. StorageTek has primarily competed with IBM in this market, and it continues to do so after its acquisition by Sun Microsystems in 2005 and again by Oracle in 2009.

Cartridge formats

Most (but not all) modern tape cartridges are made in the 3480 format, which was popularized by IBM. This is a small, rectangular and easily handled tape cartridge compared to the previously common 7-track and 9-track round tape reels. It proved rather suitable for use in automated tape libraries.

The tape is internally wound onto a single hub, mounted entirely within the external shell, and presents one end for the tape drive to engage and thread into the tape drive for reading or writing. The mechanical design of this loading mechanism varies between different types of tape media and is a common source of failures. Usually the tape cartridge incorporates a switch that can be set to permit or forbid writing of data to the tape.

It is very common for the tape cartridge to be identified by an external label or sticker, which is normally both in human readable characters such as AB1023 and also in bar code, to be read by devices in an automated library.

At the end of the tape, the drive reversed the direction of tape motion, moved the read and write heads slightly vertically across the tape, and continued to write (or read) more data until the beginning of the tape was reached. This process could be repeated many times, laying down several track sets on the tape media in a serpentine recording mode. The Storage Tek 9840, 9940 and T10000 drives are all serpentine recording drives.

The Storage Tek SD3 drive was different, being based upon a modified video recording device. The tape advanced steadily, and data was recorded (or read) by a cylindrical head rotating at high speed and inclined at a small angle to the direction of tape motion, laying down (or reading back) a series of short data tracks very closely spaced together -- helical scan.

The Storage Tek 9840 series of drives used a relatively unusual dual tape hub mechanism within the 3480 format shell, similar to the familiar audio tape format. This reduced the length of tape that could be stored inside the shell, and hence reduced the data capacity of the cartridge. However, it made the loading or threading of the tape into the drive very fast,[1] which was useful in business applications - and the drive price was set to a very high in comparison to the contemporary LTO drive, despite having one fifth of its capacity.[2]

Format	Date	Capacity (GB)	Data Rate (MB/s)	Load time (s)	Reel Configuration	Announcement
4480		0.04	3	8		
4490		0.80	4.5	8		
9490		0.40-0.80	18-20	4.3		
SD-3	1995	10-50	11-18	17		
T9840A "Eagle"	1998	20	10	12	dual reel	
T9840B	2001	20	19	12	dual reel	
T9840C	2003	40	30	12	dual reel	
T9840D	2008	75	30	16.5	dual reel	
T9940A	2000	60	10	59	single reel	
T9940B	2002	200	30	59	single reel	
T10000	2006	500	120	62	single reel	[3]

T10000B	2008	1000	120	62	single reel	[4]

These tape formats are popular in mainframe environments.[2] Drives used ESCON, FICON, Fibre Channel, or SCSI interfaces.

SD-3 (Redwood)

This format used helical scan on a 1/2 inch tape. Three different capacities of tape cartridge were offered: 10, 25 and 50 GB, differing only in the length of tape wound on the reels and in the external media identification character, A, B or C, which was designed to be read by the Powderhorn automated library's bar-code reader system.

The drive was based on a professional Panasonic video recording system, modified to be suitable for digital data recording.[5] The result was a large, heavy drive of considerable complexity. Although somewhat difficult to maintain, it won popularity among some users due to the relatively low cost of the media per Gigabyte.

SD-3 drive retired from use in a Powderhorn library

T10000

The T10000 is the latest StorageTek's tape drive and cartridge for mainframe systems. It holds 500 GB (native) and can transfer data at 120 MB/s (native).[6] Sun's aim is to provide cartridge compatibility across two successor generations; the first step toward this goal was with the announcement of the T10000B drive[4], which stores 1 TB (native) on the same cartridges as used by the T10000 drive, at the same native performance of 120 MB/s.

Close-up of the recording head of the SD-3 drive

References

[1] Austerberry, David (2003). *Digital asset management* (http://books.google.pl/books?id=G-iH2yaz29EC&pg=PA257&dq=storagetek+tape&cd=6#v=onepage&q=storagetek tape&f=false). London: Focal. pp. pp. 257. ISBN 0-240-51924-8. .

[2] Apicella, Mario (2001-11-12). "Fast, flexible, expensive" (http://books.google.pl/books?id=1TgEAAAAMBAJ&pg=PA65&dq=storagetek+tape&cd=4#v=onepage&q=storagetek tape&f=false). *InfoWorld* **23** (46): 65. . Retrieved 2010-02-22.

[3] http://www.sun.com/smi/Press/sunflash/2006-03/sunflash.20060314.1.xml

[4] http://www.sun.com/aboutsun/pr/2008-07/sunflash.20080714.2.xml

[5] Saffady, William (1998). *Managing electronic records*. ARMA International. pp. pp. 36. ISBN 0-933887-77-9.

[6] "Data Sheet Sun StorageTek T10000 Tape Drive" (https://www.sun.com/storage/docs/TC0049D_T10Kdrive_DS.pdf). . Retrieved 2010-02-22.

Sun Certified Professional

Sun Certified Professional (SCP) is a professional certification program by Sun Microsystems, a subsidiary of Oracle Corporation. It is meant to verify a particular skillset in Sun technologies, especially the Java programming language and the Solaris Operating System.

Java certification programs

Sun Certified Java Associate (SCJA)

The **Sun Certified Java Associate** (or **SCJA**), concentrates on basic knowledge of object oriented programming, UML, and the essentials of the Java programming language and platform. It costs approximately $300. It is targeted at newcomers to Java who are not necessarily working in technical positions, such as project managers, students, or developers for whom Java is not a primary requirement.

Sun Certified Java Programmer (SCJP)

The **Sun Certified Java Programmer (SCJP)** exam is the entry level Java exam and is a prerequisite to a number of the other Java-related certifications. **SCJP 6**, designated **CX-310-065** by Sun, was released in December 2007.

It is designed as a fairly detailed test of basic knowledge of the essentials of the Java programming language. It tests looping constructs and variables, and does not cover specific technologies such as GUI creation, Web or network programming. The exam tests how well a programmer has understood the language constructs and not the programmer's capability to write efficient algorithms.

It is assessed through an automatically administered multiple-choice test system and consists of 60 questions which the candidate has 180 minutes to answer [1]. At least 35 questions are needed to be correct to pass (around 58%)[1]. The exam is taken at a Prometric test center, and to take the test a candidate must buy a voucher from Sun (approximately US$300 in the US, but £150 (excluding VAT) in the UK, AUD 316 plus Tax in Australia, Rs. 7200 plus taxes in India) and book the test at least a week in advance[1]. The test consists of multiple choice and drag-and-drop questions, the latter comprising 20-25% of the questions[1].

The SCJP 6 exam tests a candidate on knowledge of declarations, access control, object orientation, assignments, operators, flow control, assertions, string handling, I/O, parsing, formatting, generics, collections, inner classes, threads and the JDK tools[1]. The test is available in English, Japanese, Chinese, German, Korean, Portuguese, Russian and Spanish[2].

Previous versions

There have been a number of previous versions of the **SCJP**. The current version, SCJP 6.0, is aimed at the JDK 6.0 release of Java. It introduces new topics covering Console, NavigableSet, and NavigableMap.

SCJP 5.0 (designated **CX-310-055**) was based on JDK 5. It introduced variable arguments, autoboxing, and generic types, and dropped the bit shifting topics from previous exams.

SCJP 1.4 (designated **CX-310-035**) was based on JDK 1.4. Compared to the previous version of the exam, SCJP 1.2, it dropped questions on GUI topics and shifted the emphasis towards core language features[3]. SCJP 1.4 features 61 questions to be answered within 120 minutes. 32 questions or more (52%) need to be answered correctly in order to pass.[4]

SCJP 1.2 (designated **CX-310-025**) was based on JDK 1.2, and was first live on 15 June 2000. The exam had 59 questions (both multiple choice and short answer) to be answered within two hours. The pass mark was 61 percent.[5] However, exam 310-025 has been withdrawn from the market; certified professionals can retain their certification and use the title, but this version is no longer being offered.

Sun Certified Java Developer (SCJD)

Sun Certified Java Developer (or **SCJD**) is the advanced Java programmer certification level. Unlike the easier SCJP, this level is intended to verify that the participant is able to write a real-world commercial application, solving all typical problems. It is the highest qualification that Sun confirms for the Standard Edition Java programmer. Prior to attempting certification, candidates must be certified as a Sun Certified Programmer (SCJP), any edition. It is not necessary to be a Sun Certified Java Associate prior to taking this exam.[6] The total cost of the exam is around $575.

The certification consists of the practical programming task and the subsequent written theory exam. The participant must write the described application, extensively using custom file formats, distributed computing (JRMP) and advanced Swing features that are not fully accessible from the popular rapid development tools (JTable, component data models and so on). The code must be documented, and the user manual must be supplied. The task itself is written in the form of a PRD for a non-programming end user. Apart from one or two interfaces, no technical details are given.

The participant is not allowed to use CORBA, RMI-IIOP, web browsers and third party libraries of any kind, because these might make a task too easy and are also subject of other certifications. He or she is allowed to use any preferred Java IDE. There used to be no strict time limit for this exam, but from May 2009 a time limit of one year has been introduced. Participants who have obtained their assignment voucher before the mentioned date, can claim to upload their solution after one year, but will need to contact SUN Microsystems. A participant in this program is expected to spend several weeks writing the program. The main disadvantage of this certification is that the participant must invest the considerable amount of work (at least several weeks) in writing that program. After the solution has been uploaded the participant must do an essay exam at a testing center, in which (s)he must answer some questions about how the solution was made. The goal of the essay exam is to determine whether the participant, who has to identify himself with an identity piece, really is the one who made the solution. The answers given will be compared with the documentation uploaded with the solution. The review of the solution, and the answers given at the essay exam, will only start after the essay exam has been submitted.

It takes up two months for the certification to be approved to allow time for the source code to be thoroughly examined.

Sun Certified Web Component Developer (SCWCD)

The **Sun Certified Web Component Developer** (**SCWCD**) certification targets information regarding Java components related to web-applications, specifically Servlets and Java Server Pages (JSPs). To achieve this certification, the candidate must pass a computer-based test available world-wide at Prometric test centers.

The SCWCD 1.4 exam covers the Java 2 Enterprise Edition (J2EE) version 1.4 code, corresponding to Servlet version 2.4 and JSP version 2.0.

SCWCD 5 was released in early 2008. The exam consists of 69 questions with 70% or above being required to pass. The time duration is 3 hours. The objectives are identical to the previous (1.4) version of the exam.

Sun Certified Business Component Developer (SCBCD)

The **Sun Certified Business Component Developer** (**SCBCD**) certification targets information regarding Java components related to distributed applications, specifically Enterprise Java Beans (EJBs). To achieve this certification, the candidate must pass a computer-based test available world-wide at Prometric test centers.

SCBCD 1.4 exam covers Java 2 Enterprise Edition (J2EE) version 1.3 code, including EJB version 2.0.

As of 2008, the SCBCD covers the Java 2 Enterprise Edition (J2EE) version 5 code, corresponding to EJB version 3.0.

The pre-requisite for this certification is that the candidate should be a Sun Certified Programmer for Java 2 Platform (any edition).

SCBCD for J2EE version 1.3 is now no longer offered (starting February 2008). However, the upgrade exam from SCBCD for J2EE version 1.3 to Java EE version 5 is still available

Sun Certified Developer for Java Web Services (SCDJWS)

The **Sun Certified Developer for Java Web Services 5** (**SCDJWS**) certification exam (designated **CX-310-230**) is for developers who have been creating web services applications using Java technology components such as those supported by the Java Web Services Developer Pack, JAX-WS and JAXB. Other topics like XML, JSON, REST and security are covered too.

There was an older version, **SCDJWS 1.4** (designated **CX-310-220**), which is already discontinued [7] , it covered topics which are now obsolete (e.g., the JAX-RPC API has been replaced by JAX-WS).

The pre-requisite for this certification is that the candidate should be a Sun Certified Programmer for Java 2 Platform (any edition). There is no dedicated book available for the exam.

Sun Certified Mobile Application Developer (SCMAD)

The **Sun Certified Mobile Application Developer** (**SCMAD**) certification targets information related to developing Mobile applications, through platform Java 2 Micro Edition (J2ME). It focuses in specifications like JTWI, CLDC, MIDP, WMA and MMAPI. SCMAD Exam Guide is the only book that focus on the exam objectives.[8]

Sun Certified Enterprise Architect (SCEA)

Sun Certified Enterprise Architect for the Java EE Platform (**SCEA**) certification certifies the skills of a software architect in the Java Enterprise Edition technology (formerly J2EE). Obtaining the certification requires the candidate to pass three individual stages:

- a multiple choice exam on the basic concepts of Java EE technology
- a UML design project involving Java EE technology
- an essay exam regarding the design project

The multiple-choice exam can be taken at any Prometric testing center around the world. Passing of this portion is required prior to registering with Sun Microsystems for the design project, which is downloaded from a secured website. After completion of the assignment and upload to the same secured website, the candidate then sits for an essay exam, once again through a Prometric test center. As the questions on the essay exam are based on the assignment for Part II, it is advised to take the essay exam as soon as possible after submitting the assignment. (The last two steps are essentially one step since they are graded in unison.) Scores for the Part I exam are known immediately after taking the test; however, the scores for Parts II/III are only available after six to eight weeks through Sun's certification manager website.

SUN released the Java EE 5 version of the SCEA exam in February 2008, and the prior version (for J2EE 1.2) was retired on March 1, 2008. Candidates who already began work on the prior track had until the end of 2008 to complete their assignments, assuming they have purchased the vouchers prior to the retirement date. Sun has also made available an upgrade track consisting of a single, multiple-choice exam not unlike the Part I examination, for those who have the prior credential. Also, unlike the prior version, a candidate for the SCEA for Java EE 5 now must complete the Part II assignment within one year - the prior version had no time limit for the assignment.

Unlike other higher-level Java exams, this certification does not require passing the Sun Certified Java Programmer exam as a prerequisite. This is due to the different job-role an architect fills on the software development team.

Should the candidate pass, Sun will award the person the status of a professional Java architect. Unlike some other technology exams (such as MCSE), this exam and all of the other Sun Java exams do not have an expiration date.

Solaris Operating System Certifications

Sun Certified Solaris Associate

The **Sun Certified Solaris Associate** (or **SCSAS**), is a newly-introducted certification for university students and other beginners seeking to gain basic knowledge of UNIX with a Solaris Operating System (Solaris OS) emphasis. Candidates will learn basic UNIX commands and tasks, performed in the Solaris OS environment.

This certification is offered for the Solaris 10 OS, consisting of one multiple choice exam.There are no prerequisites to this exam.

Sun Certified System Administrator for the Solaris Operating System

The **Sun Certified System Administrator for Solaris** (or **SCSA**), the oldest of Sun's certifications, concentrates on in depth knowledge of the Solaris OS including knowledge of basic UNIX and Solaris OS commands management of file systems, system boot and shutdown, software install, user creation and administration, security, network printers and system processes, and system backups and restores. The test covers topics of system administration for SPARC, x64, and x86 based systems. The certification requires passing score on two separate tests, Sun Certified System Administrator for Solaris 10 OS, Part I [9], (exam number 310-200), and Sun Certified System Administrator for Solaris 10 OS, Part II [10], (exam number 310-202). The certification is targeted at System Administrators working in technical positions in the Solaris OS.

Sun Certified Network Administrator for the Solaris Operating System

The **Sun Certified Network Administrator for Solaris** (or **SCNA**), follows the Sun Certified System Administrator Certification and focuses on networking skills in the Solaris OS. This exam will test candidates on their knowledge of Network Interface Layers, Transport, Network Applications and configuring the Solaris IP Filter. It is recommended that candidates have three or more years experience in networking prior to this certification. The Solaris System Administration certification is a prerequisite for this certification. This certification requires a passing score on exam number 310-302 [11]. The certification is targeted at Network Administrators working in technical positions in the Solaris OS.

Sun Certified Security Administrator for the Solaris Operating System

The **Sun Certified Security Administrator for Solaris** (or **SCSECA**), the newest of Sun's Solaris certifications, concentrates on in depth knowledge of security features of the Solaris OS including installing security features, Process Rights Management, Solaris Cryptographic framework, and Solaris Zones. The certification is targeted at advanced administrators of Solaris environments with responsibility for security.

Others

Sun Certified Specialist Netbeans IDE

The **Sun Certified Specialist Netbeans IDE** (**SCSNI**), designated **CX-310-045** concentrates on specific knowledge of the usage and functionality of the Netbeans IDE.

References

[1] Kathy Sierra and Bert Bates, "Sun Certified Programmer for Java 6: Study Guide (Exam 310-065)", 2008, ISBN 978-0-07-159108-9

[2] Sun Certified Programmer for the Java 2 Platform, Standard Edition 6 (CX-310-065) (http://www.sun.com/training/catalog/courses/CX-310-065.xml)

[3] Khalid A. Mughal, Rolf W. Rasmussen, *Programmer's Guide to Java Certification, A: A Comprehensive Primer, Second Edition*, Addison Wesley Professional, August 04, 2003, ISBN 0-201-72828-1

[4] Marcus Green (2004-04-06). "Deep into the Basics: Tackling Sun's SCJP 1.4 Exam" (http://certcities.com/editorial/exams/story.asp?EditorialsID=86). CertCities.com. . Retrieved 2006-10-19.

[5] Christine Connolly (2001-10-03). "Hot Java: An Inside Look at the SCJP Exam" (http://certcities.com/editorial/exams/story.asp?EditorialsID=42). CertCities.com. . Retrieved 2006-10-19.

[6] Sun Certified Java Developer Page: http://www.sun.com/training/certification/java/scjd.xml

[7] CodeRanch Forum: http://www.coderanch.com/t/509184/java-Web-Services-SCDJWS/certification/SCDJWS-CX-was-retired-Prometric

[8] "SCMAD Exam Guide" (http://www.scmadbook.com) by Ko Ko Naing, Sathya Srinivasan, Chad Davis and Sivasundaram Umapathy, McGraw-Hill Education (India), 2008

[9] http://www.sun.com/training/catalog/courses/CX-310-200.xml

[10] http://www.sun.com/training/catalog/courses/CX-310-202.xml

[11] http://www.sun.com/training/catalog/courses/CX-310-302.xml

External links

- Oracle Certification Page (http://education.oracle.com/pls/web_prod-plq-dad/db_pages.getpage?page_id=39) Oracle Certification Page
- Sample Questions, Mock Exams, Simulator for Oracle/Sun Java Certifications (http://enthuware.com)
- JavaRanch SCJP FAQ (http://faq.javaranch.com/java/ScjpFaq/) Sun Java Certification FAQ from the Java Ranch website
- Javaprepare (http://www.javaprepare.com/) Preparation site for Sun Java Certification
- Certification4Career (http://www.certification4career.com/) Free SCJP Preparation: Exam simulator
- JavaQ (http://www.javaquestions.net/) Java questions: SCJP Exam simulator
- java.boot.by (http://java.boot.by) Free Java Certification Study Guides

Sun Cloud

Sun Cloud is an on-demand Cloud computing service operated by Sun Microsystems, a subsidiary of Oracle Corporation. The Sun Cloud Compute Utility provides access to a substantial computing resource over the Internet for US$1 per CPU-hour. It is based on and supports open source technologies such as Solaris 10, Sun Grid Engine, and the Java platform.

Sun Cloud delivers enterprise computing power and resources over the Internet, enabling developers, researchers, scientists and businesses to optimize performance, speed time to results, and accelerate innovation without investment in IT infrastructure.

The Sun Cloud is available worldwide. Since Sunday, March 7, 2010, the network.com web site has been inaccessible.

Suitable applications

A typical application that can run on the Compute Utility fits the following parameters:

- must be self-contained
- runs on the Solaris 10 Operating System (OS)
- is implemented with standard object libraries included with the Solaris 10 OS or user libraries packaged with the executable
  - all executable code must be available on the Compute Utility at time of execution
- runs to completion under control of shell scripts (no requirement for interactive access)
- has a total maximum size of applications and data that does not exceed 10 gigabytes
- can be packaged for upload to Sun Cloud as one or more ZIP files of 300 megabytes or smaller

Resources, jobs and runs

Resources are collections of files that contain the user's data and executable.

Jobs are a Compute Utility concept that define the elements of the unit of work that is submitted to the Sun Cloud Compute Utility. The major elements of a job include the name of the shell script controlling program execution, required arguments to the shell script, and a list of resources that must be in place for the job to run.

A run is a specific instantiation of a Job description submitted to the Sun Cloud Compute Utility. Runs occur when the job is submitted to the Compute Utility for execution.

CPU-hour

For each job one submits and runs on the Cloud, the Sun Cloud CPU usage is aggregated and then rounded up to the nearest whole hour. For example, if a job used 1000 CPUs for one minute, it would be aggregated as 1000 CPU minutes or 16.67 CPU hours. The software rounds this up to 17 hours and the job would be billed as US $17.

The Application Catalog

On March 13, 2007, Sun announced the launch of Application Catalog, an online service that allows developers and ISVs to develop and publish their applications, enabling communities of scientists and academics in life sciences, education, engineering, and other fields to accelerate innovation and complete research projects quickly and less expensively.

The Network.com Application Catalog gives users immediate online access to popular ISV and open source applications through an easy-to-use Web portal with no contractual obligation. Users can upload and run their own applications and create a personal library of favorites or take advantage of the pre-installed and configured applications giving them instant productivity. The portal gives them everything they need to conduct analysis and complete complex computational tasks to help speed scientific discovery and shorten the time to market for new products. They simply select the application, upload their data, and get results fast.

Network.com enables anyone to publish applications to the Application Catalog and take advantage of the powerful Solaris 10-based Cloud platform. Users can publish their own applications to a private library and access them whenever they want; they can also share their applications with others while retaining their data securely in their private space.

Available Applications

Applications available on the Catalog include(by category):

- General - Blender, FDS
- Computer Aided Engineering - Calculix, deal.II, Elmer Solver, Impact, FreeFEM, OFELI
- Life Sciences - BLAST, FASTA, GROMACS, Clustalw, eHITS, T-Coffee, fastDNAml, READSEQ

Examples of types of suitable applications include:

- Bio informatics
- Financial domain applications, like Monte Carlo method, Black-Scholes option pricing models
- Computer Arts, like Fractal landscape generation
- Speech synthesis applications, like Festival [1]
- Scientific applications, like Computer simulation

See also

- Big Buck Bunny - an open content animated film rendered on Sun Cloud [2] [3]
- Utility computing

References

[1] http://www.cstr.ed.ac.uk/projects/festival/
[2] "Sun's Network.com Renders Computer-Animated Movie "Big Buck Bunny"" (http://www.sun.com/aboutsun/pr/2008-06/sunflash. 20080602.1.xml). Sun Microsystems. . Retrieved 2008-06-22.
[3] "The Renderfarm (how it works)" (http://www.bigbuckbunny.org/index.php/our-renderfarm-and-how-it-works/). Blender Foundation. . Retrieved 2008-06-22.

External links

- Sun Cloud (http://www.network.com/)
- Utility Computing (http://www.sun.com/solutions/cloudcomputing/index.jsp)
- Sun Grid Engine Source (http://gridengine.sunsource.net/servlets/ProjectSource)
- Sun Grid Module Suite for NetBeans IDE (http://sungridplugin.dev.java.net/)

Sun Community Source License

The **Sun Community Source License** (**SCSL**) is a community source software licensing model designed by Sun Microsystems that covered the J2EE software development kit. Sun introduced the SCSL in 1998 to maintain compatibility within the Java platform and make code available for commercial use.[1] In 2004, Sun began to favor the simpler Java Research License for noncommercial use.[2]

The SCSL includes elements similar to an open-source license, but it has significant differences, such as a requirement that code is compatible with Java standards and commercial derivative works are subject to licensing fees. The SCSL is not considered a free software license.[3]

References

[1] Loukides, Mike (1999-03-01). "Some Thoughts on the Sun Community Source License" (http://www.oreillynet.com/pub/a/oreilly/java/news/loukides_0399.html). *O'Reilly Media.* . Retrieved 2010-04-07.

[2] LaMonica, Martin (2005-03-16). "Sun looks to sweeten Java" (http://www.zdnetasia.com/sun-looks-to-sweeten-java-39221780.htm). *ZD Net.* . Retrieved 2010-04-07.

[3] Various Licenses and Comments about Them (http://www.gnu.org/licenses/license-list.html#SunCommunitySourceLicense)

External links

- SUN COMMUNITY SOURCE LICENSE Version 2.8 (Rev. Date January 17, 2001) (http://java.sun.com/j2se/1.5.0/scsl_5.0-license.txt)

Sun Industry Standards Source License

Author	Sun Microsystems
Version	1.0
Free software	Yes
OSI approved	Yes
GPL compatible	No

The **Sun Industry Standards Source License** (SISSL) is now a retired free and open source license, recognized as such by the Free Software Foundation and the Open Source Initiative (OSI). Under SISSL, developers could modify and distribute source code and derived binaries freely. Furthermore, developers could choose to keep their modifications private or make them public. However, the SISSL is unique among OSI-approved licenses in requiring that "The Modifications which You create must comply with all requirements set out by the Standards body in effect one hundred twenty (120) days before You ship the Contributor Version." If the Modifications do not comply, SISSL becomes a copyleft license, and source must be published "under the same terms as this license [SISSL] on a royalty free basis within thirty (30) days."

Several open source projects funded by Sun Microsystems were licensed under SISSL, including OpenOffice.org, and Sun Grid Engine (SGE). Later versions of OpenOffice.org were dual-licensed under the SISSL and LGPL until the retirement of the SISSL, at which time OpenOffice.org was relicensed only under the LGPL. Sun Grid Engine appears to still be covered by the SISSL.

Sun's Chief Open Source Officer Simon Phipps announced the retirement of the license on September 2, 2005. It is now listed by OSI as "voluntarily retired" by Sun, and the OSI license page states that "Sun has ceased to use or recommend this license."[1] [2] OpenOffice.org 2.0 code, for example, is now licensed exclusively under the LGPL. Sun has developed the Common Development and Distribution License, a variant of the Mozilla Public License and has since released OpenSolaris and the GlassFish Application Server under that license.

References

[1] "Sun Industry Standards Source License (SISSL)" (http://www.opensource.org/licenses/sisslpl.php). Open Source Initiative. . Retrieved 2008-05-20.
[2] "Open Source Licenses by Category" (http://www.opensource.org/licenses/category). Open Source Initiative. . Retrieved 2008-05-20.

External links

- Sun Industry Standards Source License - Version 1.1 (http://www.openoffice.org/licenses/sissl_license.html)
- OpenOffice.org license change (http://www.openoffice.org/FAQs/license-change.html)

Wikinews Sources

- Stephen Shankland " Sun retires one open-source license (http://news.com.com/Sun+retires+one+ open-source+license/2100-7344_3-5847484.html?tag=nefd.top)". *CNET*, September 2, 2005
- " Statement on License Simplification (PDF) (http://www.openoffice.org/FAQs/license-statement.pdf)". *OpenOffice.org*, September 2, 2005
- " License Simplification FAQ (http://www.openoffice.org/FAQs/license-change.html)". *OpenOffice.org*, September 2, 2005
- Simon Phipps " Addressing Proliferation: Deeds not just Words (http://blogs.sun.com/webmink/entry/ addressing_proliferation_deeds_not_just)". *Sun Microsystems*, September 2, 2005

Sun Microsystems Laboratories

Sun Microsystems Laboratories, or **Sun Labs** is the research and development branch of Sun Microsystems.[1] It was established in 1990 by Ivan Sutherland and Robert Sproull. Currently there are facilities in Menlo Park, CA and Burlington, MA, USA. The Interim Director is Robert Sproull (as of 2006).

Sun Labs works in hi-tech areas, such as asynchronous circuits, optical communications, new web technologies, Java technologies, computer networks, etc.

References

[1] Inside Sun Labs (http://www.theregister.co.uk/2005/05/02/inside_sun_labs/), The Register (http://www.theregister.co.uk/), UK.

External links

- Sun Labs website (http://research.sun.com/)

Sun Web Developer Pack

The **Sun Web Developer Pack (SWDP)** is a collection of open source software released by Sun Microsystems for developing web applications that run on Java EE application servers. The SWDP is targeted at software developers interested in writing web applications that use Web 2.0 technologies such as Ajax, REST, Atom, and JavaScript.

Software Included in the SWDP

The SWDP consists of the following software:

- Scripting language support
  - Project Phobos, a project that allows you to write web applications in JavaScript or other scripting languages
- Ajax technologies
  - Project jMaki, a framework for creating Ajax-enabled web applications in Java, PHP, or Phobos
  - Project Dynamic Faces, a framework for creating Ajax-enabled JavaServer Faces applications
- REST
  - RESTful web services, an API for creating REST web services in Java
  - WADL
- ROME, a Java API for parsing and generating RSS and Atom web feeds
- Atom Server (The ROME Propono subproject), a prototype Java API and framework for creating a web feed server for Atom feeds

Release history

Release 1 of the SWDP was made public on March 12, 2007.

External links

- Sun Web Developer Pack home page [1]
- Documentation
  - Online SWDP Tutorial [2]
  - SWDP Tutorial bundle download [3]
  - Getting Started with the SWDP [4]
- java.net project pages
  - Project jMaki [5]
  - Project Dynamic Faces [6]
  - Project Phobos [7]
  - WADL [8]
  - ROME API [9]

References

[1] http://developers.sun.com/web/swdp/index.jsp
[2] http://developers.sun.com/web/swdp/docs/tutorial/doc/toc.html
[3] http://developers.sun.com/web/swdp/docs/tutorial/download.html
[4] http://developers.sun.com/web/swdp/docs/GettingStarted.html
[5] https://ajax.dev.java.net
[6] https://jsf-extensions.dev.java.net
[7] https://phobos.dev.java.net
[8] https://wadl.dev.java.net
[9] https://rome.dev.java.net

Sun-1

Sun-1 was the first generation of UNIX computer workstations and servers produced by Sun Microsystems, launched in May 1982. These were based on a CPU board designed by Andy Bechtolsheim while he was a graduate student at Stanford University and funded by DARPA. The Sun-1 systems ran SunOS 0.9, a port of UniSoft's UniPlus V7 port of Seventh Edition UNIX to the Motorola 68000 microprocessor, with no window system. Early Sun-1 workstations and servers used the original Sun logo, a series of red "S"s laid out in a square, rather than the more familiar purple diamond shape used later.

The first Sun-1 workstation was sold to Solo Systems in May 1982.[1] The Sun-1/100 was used in the original Lucasfilm EditDroid non-linear editing system.

Models

Sun 1/100 desktop workstation

Sun 150U rackmount server

Model	Chassis
Sun 100	7-slot Multibus (desktop)
Sun 150	15-slot Multibus (rackmount)

Hardware

The Sun 1 workstation was based on the Stanford University SUN workstation designed by Andy Bechtolsheim (advised by Vaughan Pratt and Forrest Baskett), a graduate student and co-founder of Sun Microsystems. At the heart of this design were the Multibus CPU, memory, and video display cards. The cards used in the Sun-1 workstation were a second-generation design with a private memory bus allowing memory to be expanded to 2 MB without performance degradation.

Sun 100U Cardcage

The Sun 68000 board introduced in 1982 was a powerful single-board computer. It combined a 10 MHz Motorola 68000 microprocessor, a Sun designed memory management unit (MMU), 256 KB of zero wait state memory with parity, up to 32 KB of EPROM memory, two serial ports, a 16-bit parallel port and an Intel

Multibus (IEEE 796 bus) interface in a single 12-inch-wide (300 mm), 6.75-inch-deep (171 mm) Multibus form factor.

By using the Motorola 68000 processor tightly coupled with the Sun-1 MMU the Sun 68000 CPU board was able to support a multi-tasking operating system such as UNIX. It included an advanced Sun designed multi-process two-level memory management unit with facilities for memory protection, code sharing and demand paging of memory.

The CPU board included 256 KB of memory which could be replaced or augmented with two additional memory cards for a total of 2 MB. Although the memory cards used the Multibus form factor, they only used the Multibus interface for power; all memory access was via the smaller private *P2* bus. This was a synchronous private memory bus which allowed for simultaneous memory input/output transfers. It also allowed for full performance zero wait state operation of the memory. When installing the first 1 MB expansion board either the 256 Kb of memory on the CPU board or the first 256 KB on the expansion board had to be disabled.[2]

On-board I/O included a dual serial port UART and a 16-bit parallel port. The serial ports were implemented with an Intel 8274 UART and later with a NEC D7201C UART. Serial port A was wired as a Data Communications Equipment (DCE) port and had full modem control. It was also the console port if no graphical display was installed in the system. Serial port B was wired as a Data Terminal Equipment (DTE) port and had no modem control. Both serial ports could also be used as terminal ports and quite often were allowing 3 people to use one workstation, although two did not have graphical displays. The 16-bit parallel port was a special purpose port for connecting 8-bit parallel port keyboard and 8-bit parallel port optical mouse for workstations with graphical displays. The parallel port was never used as a general purpose parallel printer port.

The CPU board included a fully compatible Multibus (IEEE 796 bus). It was an asynchronous bus that accommodated devices with various transfer rates while maintaining maximum throughput. It had 20 address lines so it could address up to 1 MB of Multibus memory and 1 MB of I/O locations although most I/O devices only decoded the first 64 KB of address space. The Sun CPU board fully supported multi-master functionality that allowed it to share the Multibus with other DMA devices.[3]

The keyboard was a Micro Switch 103SD30-2, or a KeyTronic P2441 for the German market. The memory-mapped, bit-mapped frame buffer (graphics) board had a resolution of 1024×1024 pixels, but only 1024×800 was displayed on the monitor. The graphics board included hardware to accelerate raster operations. A Ball model HD17H 17-inch video display monitor was used. An Ethernet board was available, originally implementing the 3 Mbit/s Xerox PARC Ethernet specification, which was later upgraded to the 3Com 10 Mbit/s version. An Interphase SMD 2180 disk controller could be installed to connect up to four Fujitsu 84 MB M2313K or CDC 16.7 MB (8.35 MB fixed, 8.35 MB removable) 9455 Lark drives. All of the boards were installed in a 6 or 7-slot Multibus card cage.

Later documentation shows that a 13- or 19-inch color display was available. The color frame buffer had a resolution of 640×512 pixels, with 640×480 displayed on the monitor. The board could display 256 colors from a palette of 16 million. 1/2 inch 9-track and 1/4 inch QIC-11 tape drives were also added to the offering.

There was also a second generation Sun-1 CPU board referred to as the Sun-1.5 CPU board.[4]

Sun-1 systems upgraded with Sun-2 Multibus CPU boards were identified with a *U* suffix to their model number.

References

[1] Amar Bhide, *Vinod Khosla and Sun Microsystems* (http://harvardbusinessonline.hbsp.harvard.edu/b02/en/common/item_detail.
jhtml?id=390049), Harvard Business School, USA, 14 December 1989.

[2] Sun 1M Memory Board User's Manual, Sun Microsystems, Inc., February 1983, Revision A

[3] *Sun 68000 Board User's Manual*, Sun Microsystems, February 1983, Revision B.

[4] *Sun 120/170 Installation Manual*, Sun Microsystems, March 12, 1984, Revision C.

Bibliography

* *Sun-1 System Reference Manual*, Sun Microsystems, 1982.
* Andreas Bechtolsheim, Forest Baskett, and Vaughan Pratt, The SUN Workstation Architecture (ftp://reports.
  stanford.edu/pub/cstr/reports/csl/tr/82/229/CSL-TR-82-229.pdf), Stanford University Computer Systems
  Laboratory Technical Report No. 229, March 1982.
* M. Hall, *Sunburst: The Ascent of Sun Microsystems*. Chicago, Contemporary Books, 1990. ISBN 0-8092-4368-7.

External links

* Sun Microsystems (http://www.sun.com/)
* The Sun Hardware Reference, Part 1 (http://www.sunhelp.org/faq/sunref1.html)
* Online Sun Information Archive Sun-1 page (http://www.sunstuff.org/hardware/systems/sun1/Sun-1/)
* Sun Field Engineer Handbook, 20th edition (http://www.sunshack.org/data/feh/1.5/wcd00094/wcd09477.
  htm)
* Pictures of a Sun1/100U (http://www.1000bit.net/scheda.asp?id=1958)
* Sun-1 display at Stanford University's Gates Information Science (http://infolab.stanford.edu/pub/voy/
  museum/pictures/display/SUN.htm)
* Sun-1 board images and manual PDFs (http://www.solivant.com/sun100)
* Sun 1 manuals at bitsavers.org (http://www.bitsavers.org/pdf/sun/sun1/)

Write once, run anywhere

"**Write once, run anywhere**" (**WORA**), or sometimes *write once, run everywhere* (**WORE**), is a slogan created by Sun Microsystems to illustrate the cross-platform benefits of the Java language.[1] [2] Ideally, this means Java can be developed on any device, compiled into a standard bytecode and be expected to run on any device equipped with a Java virtual machine (JVM). The installation of a JVM or Java interpreter on chips, devices or software packages has become an industry standard practice.

This means a programmer can develop code on a PC and can expect it to run on Java enabled cell phones, as well as on routers and mainframes equipped with Java, without any adjustments. This is intended to save software developers the effort of writing a different version of their software for each platform or operating system they intend to deploy on.

This idea originated as early as in the late 1970s, when the UCSD Pascal system was developed to produce and interpret p-code. UCSD Pascal (along with the Smalltalk virtual machine) was a key influence on the design of the Java virtual machine, as is cited by James Gosling.

The catch is that since there are multiple JVM implementations, on top of a wide variety of different operating systems such as Windows, Linux, Solaris, NetWare, HP-UX, and Mac OS, there can be subtle differences in how a program may execute on each JVM/OS combination, which may require an application to be tested on various target platforms. This has given rise to the joke among Java developers, "Write Once, Debug Everywhere".[3] However, for a developer, the abstraction layer that Java provides is usually more convenient than recompiling software for each combination of operating system and architecture that it should run on and still represents a significant reduction in work when developing and supporting an application on multiple platforms.

References

[1] "JavaSoft ships Java 1.0" (http://www.sun.com/smi/Press/sunflash/1996-01/sunflash.960123.10561.xml). Sun Microsystems. 1996-01-23. . Retrieved 2008-08-03. "*Java's write-once-run-everywhere capability along with its easy accessibility have propelled the software and Internet communities to embrace it as the de facto standard for writing applications for complex networks*"

[2] "Write once, run anywhere?" (http://www.computerweekly.com/Articles/2002/05/02/186793/write-once-run-anywhere.htm). Computer Weekly. 2002-05-02. . Retrieved 2009-07-27.

[3] Wong, William (2002-05-27). "Write Once, Debug Everywhere" (http://electronicdesign.com/Articles/Index.cfm?ArticleID=2255& pg=3). electronicdesign.com. . Retrieved 2008-08-03. "*So far, the "write-once, run-everywhere" promise of Java hasn't come true. The bulk of a Java application will migrate between most Java implementations, but taking advantage of a VM-specific feature causes porting problems.*"

See also

- Criticisms of cross-platform development and this slogan
- Write once, compile anywhere

  - Free Pascal
- C to Java Virtual Machine compilers
- Parrot virtual machine

Article Sources and Contributors

DB13W3 *Source*: http://en.wikipedia.org/w/index.php?oldid=391705491 *Contributors*: Airplaneman, Andrew sh, Arch dude, Atlant, BlowToad, Bumm13, Darklilac, Electron9, FreelanceWizard, Heron, Heywøød, Mattlach, Maury Markowitz, Megapixie, Mobius, Nono64, Plugwash, PrologFan, Reactor, RoySmith, StephenEdmonds, SuperDude115, Widefox, Wongm, Wtmitchell, 24 anonymous edits

D-subminiature *Source*: http://en.wikipedia.org/w/index.php?oldid=395826147 *Contributors*: ABaillieul, AJim, Aaron Lawrence, Aaronwood77, Al Lemos, Andrew sh, Andrewa, Angelic Wraith, Atlant, Auta, Beland, Bilbo1507, Binksternet, Biot, Boffy b, Bovineone, Brian Patrie, Brycen, CTarna, CanisRufus, Centrx, DARTH SIDIOUS 2, Dah31, Damian Yerrick, Deerslayer, Deville, DireWolf, Drego5, Eddyholland, Electron9, Enkauston, EtherealNinja, Evilspoons, Giraffedata, Guiddruid, Hairy Dude, Heron, Heywøød, Indon, JJC1138, John Bentley, Jonverve, Kadin2048, Karlhendrikse, Kelson, Kevin, Kubanczyk, Kyleaa, Mark Rizo, Matt.t.gorman, MegX, Mike1024, Militoy, Misternuvistor, Mobius, Moggie2002, Msauve, Mywhitekeyboard, Neonumbers, Nick, PZ, Pabouk, Pipak, Plugwash, Radiant chains, Radiojon, Rbrwr, RedWolf, RevRagnarok, Rich257, Rjwilmsi, Sam Hocevar, SandStone, Smallpond, Stephan Leeds, Supercoop, Thumperward, Tothwolf, ViperSnake151, Wernher, Whosasking, William Allen Simpson, Wtshymanski, 157 anonymous edits

Sun Microsystems *Source*: http://en.wikipedia.org/w/index.php?oldid=399057465 *Contributors*: 16@r, 216.237.32.xxx, A Man In Black, AEMoreira042281, Aboutmovies, Abu badali, Activeentity, Adinanance, Adrian, Aeons, Ahoerstemeier, Alai, Alan Millar, Alexdethier, Alexsalmond, Alrasheedan, Altenmann, Altintx, Amcl, Amren, AnandKumria, Andre Engels, Andrewpmk, AndyHedges, Angela, Angus Lepper, Anon user, Anshada, Apoc2400, Arite, Arnies, Aron Håkanson, Arpa, Ash, Ashishag, Atlant, Audriusa, Auroranorth, Awatt6, Azeemj, Balajesankar, Bash, Baumi, Bboyskidz, Beland, Benjamin Mako Hill, Benuski, Birkett, Bissinger, Bleakcomb, Blehfu, Bobblewik, Bongomatic, Boothy443, Bovineone, Boxstaa, Brion VIBBER, BrownHairedGirl, CambridgeBayWeather, Camilo Sanchez, CanisRufus, Careful Cowboy, CaribDigita, Catapult, Cbruno, CeciliaPang, Centrx, Chaitanya.lala, Chealer, Cheesy mike, Chris Mercieca, Chris the speller, ChrisRuvolo, Chrisn4255, Christian List, Christopher Mahan, Christophersaul, Chriswiki, Claytonjr, Cleduc, Cometstyles, CommonsDelinker, Conti, Conversion script, Coolcaesar, Cornflake pirate, Creidieki, Creynard, Csabo, Cyan, Cybercobra, DMG413, Damian Yerrick, David Gerard, David Richard Bell, DavidHalko, DavidJackson, Delirium, Denny, Derek56, Digisus, Dori, Doze, Dpv, Dreamyshade, Dyl, Edcolins, Edward, Egil, Ehn, ElTyrant, Elmo40, Elving, Enharmonix, Enigmaman, EoGuy, Eric-Wester, Esjones, Espen, Esuqi, EugeneZelenko, Ewlyahoocom, EwokiWiki, Ff1959, Fiftyquid, Finlay McWalter, Flashatsystemnews, Fleminra, Fourdee, Fraggle81, Fragilityfemme, Franckn55, Frap, Fredrik, Freedom to share, Frodet, Fudoreaper, Fuhghettaboutit, Funandtrvl, GDibyendu, Galoubet, Gardar Rurak, Gentgeen, Geographer, Geopgeop, Ghettoblaster, Gkanel, Glennklockwood, Gracenotes, Graham87, Greenrd, Greenshed, GreenwoodKL, Ground Zero, Guaka, Gunnar Larsson, Guy Harris, Gwernol, Hansivers, Happyfeet10, Harvester, Headbomb, Hergio, Hidro, Hoane, HubmaN, Hughey, Hydrargyrum, I5bala, InShaneee, Indolering, Int21h, Ipoengzadik, Ipsign, Isnow, J, J Di, J.delanoy, JFinigan, JLaTondre, JVz, Jamcib, Jcea, Jddimarco, Jdpf, Jebba, Jeff G., JeffV, Jeronimo, Jerryseinfeld, Jesse Viviano, Jimb 1234, Jjaazz, Jjolsen, Jnymcgee, Joffeloff, John Vandenberg, John of Reading, Johnrambo3, Jonson,William, JorgeGG, Jose Icaza, Josephw, Jpkotta, Jsavit, Justins123, KUsam, Kaaveh Ahangar, Kaysov, Kkm010, Koman90, Kopf1988, Kosmatiy, Kpjas, Kristof vt, Ksmathers, Kstailey, Kvgd, LAX, Lee Pavelich, Leomyhero, Letdorf, Lightmouse, Llort, Lotje, LtNOWIS, Lupin, Lvizon, Lykovaa, M gol, MER-C, Maksudu235, MariaMitchell, MarkMLl, Markcollinsx, Marnanel, Martarius, Martinkunev, Matt Heard, Maxsta63, Mb1000, Mditto, Mehudson1, Mellum, Mfaridh, Michael93555, Minesweeper, Minghong, Mion, Mjb, Mopashinov, Mortense, Mrbill, Mre5765, Msalciccia, Mschel, Mschlindwein, Mshonle, Mturk, Mulad, Mushroom, Mwtoews, Mythdon, Nakakapagpabagabag, NapoliRoma, NeilN, Neilc, NemethE, Nick125, Nixdorf, Noypi380, Number29, Nurg, Nwbeeson, Off!, Ofus, Olivier, One, Oo64eva, PL290, Paul Magnussen, Paulinho28, PeteVerdon, Pgilman, PhilipMW, Phobos11, Pietnoll, Pig de Wig, Pip11, Pit, Pmsyyz, Popsracer, Poweroid, Quadra630, Quarl, Qwertyus, R'n'B, RadicalBender, Raghavsuryadev, Rajington, Raysonho, Rchrd, Reisio, Rfc1394, Rich Farmbrough, Rick Block, Rilak, Rjensen, Rjw62, Rjwilmsi, Rkinch, Rob1974, Robert.Harker, Robguru, RobyWayne, Ronark, Ronz, Roscoe x, Rufus843, Ryan Norton, Ryjaz, SMadhab, SNIyer12, Sadel2000, Samsara, Sceptre, Scientus, Scwlong, Seth Nimbosa, ShadowHntr, Sherool, Sigbusyff, SimonLyall, Simosx, Simple Bob, Skierpage, Slady, Slambo, Slashme, SlimVirgin, Spellmaster, Spurdayn, SpuriousQ, Squash Racket, Stacalusa, Stanleylieber, Stepheng3, Stev0, Stevey7788, StuartBrady, Suisui, Superm401, Suzannemasterson, Swerling, TAnthony, TakuyaMurata, Tascha96, Telso, Thatdog, The Anome, The Pedant, The Thing That Should Not Be, The wub, Thegreatglobetrotter, Thepangelinanpost, Thfr, Thivierr, Thumperward, Tigeron, TimBray, TimTay, Timc, Tkaizan, Tkgd2007, Tmd, Toddschu, Tonywalton, Toussaint, Tregoweth, TwoOneTwo, Urbanrenewal, UtherSRG, Uucp, Uzume, Vanished user 34958, Vegaswikian, Vespristiano, Vjanand, Vocaro, Vunzmstr, Vzolin, Warofdreams, Watch5xer, Wdyoung, Webmink, WeisheitSuchen, Wernher, Wfpoulet, WhisperToMe, Wikievil666, Wknight94, Wolfstu, Xmachina, Yellowdesk, ZakuSage, ZimZalaBim, Zmiller923, Zoeb, Zr2d2, 482 anonymous edits

List of display interfaces *Source*: http://en.wikipedia.org/w/index.php?oldid=218036009 *Contributors*: Airplaneman, AndyFinkenstadt, Arnoldp, Beland, Bollinger, Brycen, CommonsDelinker, DMahalko, Dinjiin, Dosman, Electron9, Evan-Amos, FT2, Fallschirmjäger, Fox89, Frank.vanMeurs, Fudoreaper, Fxhomie, Gioto, GrandDrake, Guy Harris, J M Rice, Joeinwap, Joeloliv8, John Bentley, Joshuaali, Keenan Pepper, Lightmouse, Lx45803, Macbookair3140, Markphahn, Mrnatural, Nono64, Nyttend, Pmsyyz, RBBrittain, Radek Podgorny, Rajnr, Rjwilmsi, Rprpr, Rtwhite, Rwwww, Rythie, SETH HIKARU, Signalhead, Startswithj, Tnxman307, Tyler9xp, Woohookitty, YppinS, Zilog Jones, 46 anonymous edits

Sun acquisition by Oracle *Source*: http://en.wikipedia.org/w/index.php?oldid=391235963 *Contributors*: Altenmann, Cybercobra, Edcolins, NapoliRoma, Pino, TonyW, 30 anonymous edits

Agnews Developmental Center *Source*: http://en.wikipedia.org/w/index.php?oldid=388203655 *Contributors*: Acroterion, Ajraddatz, Ebyabe, EugeneZelenko, Finlay McWalter, Grutness, Hmains, Johnpacklambert, Jordan Brown, Lightmouse, Look2See1, Mditto, NapoliRoma, Natgoo, Orlady, PKT, Pietnoll, Plasma east, Rich Farmbrough, S. M. Sullivan, Sardanaphalus, Stepheng3, StonewallCanyon, TJRC, Taggard, Tarc, TimTay, 11 anonymous edits

Cobalt Networks *Source*: http://en.wikipedia.org/w/index.php?oldid=321125565 *Contributors*: Akc9000, Andy M. Wang, Doctorwillis, Elonka, Ewlyahoocom, GregorB, Malcolma, NJJ.Rocher, NapoliRoma, Noypi380, Rdarlington, Rich Farmbrough, Rilak, Romanc19s, ShadowHntr, Spike Wilbury, SpuriousQ, Steventee, Valrith, Xtifr, 16 anonymous edits

Elbrus (computer) *Source*: http://en.wikipedia.org/w/index.php?oldid=399578369 *Contributors*: A5b, Alecv, Altenmann, Antonrojo, Arch dude, Bichito, CommonsDelinker, Crocodilicus, Error, Gar3t, Gene Nygaard, Gene s, Hellisp, Jerzy, Jpbowen, Lightmouse, Mmccalpin, Monedula, Mrwojo, Piv-pro, Russavia, Saiht, Suruena, Tec15, Toresbe, Wernher, Witbrock, Yonkie, Yuriybrisk, ²¹², 18 anonymous edits

List of Sun Microsystems employees *Source*: http://en.wikipedia.org/w/index.php?oldid=368969467 *Contributors*: Ade oshineye, Alainr345, Alanc, Anon user, Benjamin Mako Hill, Bradadoopy, Centrx, Chealer, Cheesy mike, Closedmouth, Dyl, Edcolins, Imadaman, Java22, Jpbowen, Kkm010, Makeemlighter, Midom, NapoliRoma, Nono64, Pheeboris, Rwwww, Sbscottw, Schultmc, Shadowlynk, Tech.contrarian, Timurite, Toddst1, Toussaint, Ulric1313, UnitedStatesian, Webmink, Woodjr, Xmlizer, 37 anonymous edits

Java (programming language) *Source*: http://en.wikipedia.org/w/index.php?oldid=399504665 *Contributors*: -Barry-, 16@r, 172.176.26.xxx, 1exec1, 1wolfblake, 4twenty42o, 7, =JaCyX=, @modi, ABCD, AJim, Aaron Bowen, Aaron Rotenberg, Abarnea 2000, Abelson, Adam1213, AdamH, Adamacious, Adashiel, Addaintstopnme, Addshore, Aditya, AdjustShift, Adw2000, Ae-a, Aeons, Aesopos, Agrawaam, Ahoerstemeier, Air pacquiao, Aitias, Aiyizo, Aka042, Akamad, Akersmc, Aksi great, Aktsu, Alai, Alainr345, Alan Rockefeller, Alansohn, AlbertCahalan, Alerante, Alex LE, Alex.atkins, Alex.muller, Alexdethier, Alexius08, Alfio, Alhoori, Alicam8, AlistairMcMillan, Allan McInnes, Alterego, Altmany, Alvin-cs, Am088, Amareto2, Amazon911, Ambarishmohan, Amicon, Amire80, Amitchaudhary, Ammubhave, Ancheta Wis, Andonic, Andre Engels, Andrea Parri, Andres, Andrewferrier, Andrewlp1991, Andypandy.UK, Anger22, Angusmclellan, Anirudhsshastry, Anirudhvyas010, Anizzah, Anon lynx, Anoopan, Antaeus Feldspar, Antandrus, Antidrugue, Anwar saadat, Aphonik, Arabic Pilot, Arbitrarily0, ArchMageZeratuL, ArchNemesis, Archenzo, Ardonik, Ardric47, Aremith, Arloz, Armando82, Arnehans, Arrenlex, AscendantOat, Asuhaspatil, Austin Hair, Averell23, B3t, BBUCommander, Baa, Babarcash, Babedacus, Babomb, Bacchus87, Bachmann1234, Bact, Badgernet, Banaticus, Baricom, Baronnet, BarretBonden, Basitj, Batneil, Bboy123, Bcrowell, Bedel23, Belem tower, Ben Arnold, BenAveling, Benhocking, Beno1000, Betacommand, Bevo, Biblbroks, BigGuyC, Bijee, Biker Biker, Billy On Bannana Peels, Biot, Bissinger, Blablablob, Blankfrack, Bluemoose, Blurpeace, Bobblewik, Bobo192, Boing! said Zebedee, Booyabazooka, Borislav, Bovlb, Bravegag, Brick Thrower, Brion VIBBER, Brossow, BruceMagnus, Bubba-, Buchanan-Hermit, Bulatych, BurntSky, Burzmali, Byronknoll, Bytbox, CAkira, Cal 1234, Calvin 1998, Calvinaustin, Canadafreakazoid, CanadianLinuxUser, Cananian, Candear, CanisRufus, Cap'n Refsmmat, CapitalR, Capricorn42, CaribDigita, Casperl, Cat-five, Catamorphism, Catgut, Cburnett, Centrx, CesarB, Cgs, Chandrasekar78, Chaotic cultist, Charles Matthews, CharlesC, Chasingsol, Chazwatson, Chealer, Cheesy mike, Chei, Cheung1303, Chinhnt2k3, Chiok, Chip Zero, Chiprunner, Chocolateboy, Chowbok, Chrislk02, Chrissyboi, ChristianEdwardGruber, ChristopheS, Christopher Mahan, Chu Jetcheng, Chuayw2000, Chuq, Chzz, ClanCC, Classical Esther, Cleared as filed, ClockworkLunch, Closedmouth, Clydedoris, Coffee, Coley s, Cometstyles, Connelly, Conor H., Conversion script, Coolshit, Corpx, Corti, Cp98ak, Cpl Syx, Crazz bug 5, Creidieki, CunningLinguist, Cureden, Curmudgeon99, Curps, Cwfrei, Cwolfsheep, Cyan, Cybercobra, CyborgTosser, Cynic783, Cyp, Cyrius, D'Agosta, D6, DARTH SIDIOUS 2, DJ Clayworth, DMacks, DNewhall, Daf, Daimengrui, Damian Yerrick, Dan aka jack, Danakil, Dancraggs, Danhash, Daniel Brockman, Daniel.Cardenas, DanielTrox, Danrah, Darklilac, Dave Runger, David Gerard, Davidjk, Davidweiner23, Dawnseeker2000, Dbiagioli, Dcoetzee, Dcprice555, DeadEyeArrow, Debajit, Debashish, Debeo Morium, Decagon, Delian31, Delirium, Delldot, Delta G, DennisWithem, Derek farn, DetlevSchm, Dgies, Dgwarwick, Dhoom, Diberri, Dibujon, Diderot's dreams, DigiPen92, Dillard421, DineshMungra, Dingskes, Dipet343, Discospinster, Djsuess, Dll99, Dmyersturnbull, Dominic7848, Don-vip, Donama, Dongiulio, Doradus, Doug Bell, Dpark, Dr-unifex, DrIdiot, Drakkos, Drappel, Dreadstar, Dream of Goats, DreamGuy, Drmies, DropDeadGorgias, Dterei, Dumitru Gherea, Dysprosia, Dystopianray, Eagleal, Easyas12c, EbulaJonez, Ed Poor, Edcolins, Edknol, Edward, EdwardMcBride, Edwin.wei, Efriedman, Egomaniac, Eik Corell, Ekashp, ElBenevolente, Elf, Ellenaz, Ellmist, Eloquence, Elvarg, Ems2, Enchanter, EngineerScotty, Enough2000, EpiQ SkiLL, Er Komandante, ErKURITA, Errandir, Ervinn, Essjay, Ethridgela, Etz Haim, Euchiasmus, Everyking, Evice, Evil Monkey, Evil saltine, Evildeathmath, Excirial, Fabriciodosanjossilva, FactChecker1199, Fagstein, Fakahi, Falcon300000, Falcon8765, Fang Aili, Fasga, Fashionslide, Fast.ch, Fasten, Favonian, Fennec, Ferdinand Pienaar, Feureau, Ff1959, Fieldday-sunday, Finlay McWalter, Flamingantichimp, Flash200, FlavioMattos, FlavrSavr, Fleminra, Florentyna, Fogger, Fotinakis, Frap, Frecklefoot, Fredrik, Freedom to share, FreplySpang, Ftiercel, Fuchsias, Funandtrvl, Furrykef, Fx2, Gail, Gaius Cornelius, Galaxy001, Galwhaa, Gamma, Gary King, Garygateaux, Garyzx, Gazwim, Gdavidp, Ged UK, Geekler, Generalguy11, Georgia guy, Giftlite, Gilgamesh, Gimme danger, Gimmekat, Givegains, Glasser, Glenn Maddox, Glezos, Gmoore19, GnuDoyng, Gogo Dodo, Gortsack, Gracenotes, GraemeL, Graffity, Grandscribe, Graue, Great Cthulhu, Green caterpillar, Green meklar, Greenrd, Gronky, Grunt, Gscshoyru, Gudeldar, Gurch, Gurklurk, Gutworth, Guusbosman, Guy Peters, Guyjohnston, Gwern, Gzkn, Gökhan, H-b-g, H4xx0r, Hadal, Haham hanuka, HalfShadow, Hao2lian, HappyInGeneral, Hara100, Hariva, Harm.frielink, HarmonicSphere, HarryAlffa, Harshadoak, Haseo9999,

Havarhen, Hayabusa future, Hdante, Hedoluna, Henning Makholm, Henrygb, HereToHelp, Hervegirod, Hfastedge, Hgfernan, Hirudo, Hirzel, Hmains, HoganLong, Hooperbloob, Hosterweis, Hrshtkumar, Hu12, Husond, IBlender, Ideogram, Imaginationac, Immunize, Int19h, Ioakar, Iodine, Iridescent, Irish Souffle, Irishguy, Ishanthasiribaddana, J Di, J.J.Sagnella, J.delanoy, J.l.barthel, J7, JEBrown87544, JHeinonen, JIP, JLaTondre, JOptionPane, JTN, JWaide, Jabberrock, Jaglnx, JamesBWatson, Jamesday, Jarchitect, Java jack jan, Javageek212, Javawizard, Jay, Jay Gatsby, Jaybee, Jaydeki, Jcw69, Jdforrester, Jeff G., Jeffq, Jeffrey Mall, Jeffuit, Jeltz, Jemijohn, JenniferHeartsU, Jeronimo, Jesse Viviano, JesseHogan, Jglick, Jibjibjib, Jijithp, JimWae, Jimguot, Jiy, Jj137, Jjaazz, Jleedev, Jmendez, Joelr31, Joerite, John Hendrikx, John Vandenberg, JohnCongerton, Johnuniq, Jojit fb, Jonabbey, Jonathanischoice, Jondel, Jonik, Jopo sf, JorgePeixoto, Joseph Solis in Australia, JoshHolloway, Joshisachin79, Jsavit, Juansempere, Julian Mendez, Junes, Jusdafax, Justforasecond, KUsam, Kaldari, Kamalraja, Kamasutra, Kariteh, Karl-Henner, Kbolino, Kcirb, Kedit1181, Keith Azzopardi, KelleyCook, Kevin Saff, Keycard, Khakipuce, Khalid hassani, Killick, Kingturtle, Kkm010, Kks krishna, Klausness, Klingpl0x, KnowledgeOfSelf, Knyf, Kona1611, Koyaanis Qatsi, Kozuch, Kprobst, Kula85, Kungfuadam, Kurrgo master of planet x, Kuru, Kvdveer, Kwaku, Kwalsh5, Kyle Baggs, LFaraone, Landryhc, Lavellem, Leafyplant, LeaveSleaves, Lee Daniel Crocker, Lee J Haywood, LeeHunter, LeilaniLad, Lerdthenerd, LestatdeLioncourt, Levin, Lights, Little Mountain 5, LittleDan, Loadmaster, Logariasmo, Loizbec, Lpetrazickis, Lucas Malor, Luk, Lukejea, Lumingz, Luna Santin, Lupin, Lysander89, M1chu, M4gnum0n, MER-C, MIT Trekkie, MYC36, MaBe, Magicfox13, Magioladitis, Magister Mathematicae, Magnus Manske, Mahanga, MaikSchreiber, Mailer diablo, Mainepenguin, Majorly, Malcohol, Mani1, Maoj-wsu-MC, MarSch, MarXidad, Maraist, Marcelbutucea, Marcoandre, Mark Harrison, Mark Renier, MarkSweep, Marky1981, Marlow4, Martarius, Marteau, Marty360, Maryo1912, Massysett, Matherson, MattGiuca, Matthew Yeager, Matthewpun, Matthieu fr, Mav, Max Schwarz, MaxEnt, Maxim, Mcclain, Meara, Mecanismo, MeekMark, Meekohi, Melnakeeb, Melsaran, Menchi, Mentifisto, Metamorf, Mfb52, Mhorlbec, Michaelneale, Mikademus, Mike0001, Mikelo.Arbaro, Mikm, Minesweeper, Minghong, Minipie8, Minkythecat, Minute Lake, Mipadi, Mirror Vax, Misantropo, Misza13, Mitchellfx, Mjroots, Modster, Modulatum, Mohamedloey, Mohsens, Molteanu, Momet, Monkbel, MoraSique, Morte, Morwen, Mr link, MrCoder, MrJones, Mritunjai, Mrstonky, Msusmangani, Mtleslie, MuZemike, Mucus, Mxn, Myanw, Mzajac, N4te, NJM, Naddy, Nanshu, NapoliRoma, NathanBeach, Ncmathsadist, Neilc, Nephelin, Nephtes, Neurolysis, NevilleDNZ, NewEnglandYankee, Newsmaestro, Nick R Hill, Nick125, NickBush24, Nigelj, Nikai, Nikhil.bandekar, Nil Einne, Nimur, Nixeagle, Nmrd, Nnp, NoirNoir, Nopetro, Npovmachine, Ntsimp, NuclearWarfare, Nwbeeson, Oatmealcookiemon, Oblivious, Odinjobs, Ohnoitsjamie, OlEnglish, Oldadamml, Oleg Alexandrov, Oli Filth, Oneforfortytwo, Onehundredandtwo, Onevalefan, Opt 05, Orderud, Orisino, OscarTheCat3, OwenBlacker, OwenX, Oysterguitarist, P-unit, P0lyglut, PGibbons, PMJain, Pagingmrherman, Pascalv, Patman g, Patrick987, Paul Murray, Paul Richter, Paul99, Paules nl, Pavel Vozenilek, Pawan shanku, Peepeedia, Pengo, PerLundberg, Perfecto, Peter Delmonte, Peter Griffin, Peter lawrey, Peterl, Pgk, PhageRules1, Phantomsteve, Pharos, Phgao, Phil websurfer@yahoo.com, PhilKnight, Philipwhiuk, Phoenix-forgotten, Piano non troppo, Piet Delport, Pigpigking, Pinktulip, Pipedreamergrey, Pizza Puzzle, Plugwash, PlusMinus, Pmronchi, Pne, Poccil, Polluxian, Polydor, Pontillo, Poor Yorick, Potatoj316, Premvvnc, Priyankgokani, Pro Grape, Professor Calculus, Proficient, ProvingReliabilty, Public Menace, Pundeerd, PuzzletChung, Pwooster, Quadell, Quantumelfmage, Qwertyus, Qwyrxian, R3m0t, Rab8613, Raistlin11325, RandalSchwartz, Ranjith16, Rao crazy, Raul654, Ravchit, Raveendra Lakpriya, Raven4x4x, Raynoism, Rccarman, Rcs, Rdsmith4, Real-Life Sock Puppet, RedWolf, RedZombie125, Redrocket, Redvers, Reisio, Rettetast, RexNL, Rgeorgy, Rhobite, RichF, Rick Jelliffe, Risk one, Rjmfernandes, Rjwilmsi, Robert Merkel, Robert Skyhawk, RobertG, Robo.mind, Rodhullandemu, Rogerd, Ron mmi, Ronz, RossPatterson, Rossmann, RoyBoy, Rror, Rtanz, Rufous, Ruiz, Ruud Koot, Rzwitserloot, S-n-ushakov, SAE1962, SF007, SGNDave, SNIyer12, ST47, Sam Hocevar, Sam Korn, Sam jervis, Samohyl Jan, San25872, Santiago Roza (Kq), Saravask, Sasha Slutsker, Sass24, Satanjava, Scarian, Schissel, SchnitzelMannGreek, Scientus, Scjessey, Scm83x, Scovetta, Sdfisher, Sdornan, SeanJA, Seanhan, Search4Lancer, Sebastiangarth, Seraphimblade, Sfmontyo, Shadowjams, Shenme, Siddartha.kaja, Sigma 7, SimonP, Sinn, Sir Anon, SirWoland, Siroxo, Sirworthyduck, Sj, Sjarosz, Sjc, SkyWalker, Sleske, Slike, SlitherM, Smyth, Snowolf, Socablg2, SocratesJedi, Sohil it, Some P. Erson, Soptep, Spalding, Sparker046, Speedogoo, Spencer, Spiff, SpikeToronto, Spookfish, Spoon!, Spug, Squingynaut, Starblind, Starwiz, Steffen Felbinger, Stephen, Stephen B Streater, Stereo, Stevenj, Stevenrasnick, Stevietheman, Stormie, Styrofoam1994, Subanark, Suffusion of Yellow, Sunderland06, Super Quinn, SuperU, Superfly Jon, Superm401, Supernova17, Supertouch, Susvolans, SvGeloven, Swintrob, Sylent, Synthiac, Szajd, TOReilly, TRauMa, TakuyaMurata, Talandor, Tar5047, Tariqabjotu, Tasc, TastyPoutine, Tcgunner90, Tcncv, Teabeard, Technopat, Tedickey, Tellyaddict, Template namespace initialisation script, TerokNor, Terrible Tim, Testmod1, The Anome, The Elves Of Dunsimore, The Hokkaido Crow, The Thing That Should Not Be, The wub, The1physicist, The2ndflood, TheDarkArchon, TheSpook, Thehelpfulone, Theresa knott, Theuser, Thingg, Thornelytaylor, Thue, Thumperward, Thunderbolt16, Tillmo, Tim1988, TimTay, Timwhit, Titoxd, Tjansen, Tkgd2007, Tlim7882, Tmaher, Tmbg37, Tom 99, Tommy2010, Tompsci, Torc2, Tothwolf, Toussaint, Toytoy, Tresiden, Troels Arvin, Tthorley, Ttwaring, Turing, Tushar.kute, Tustin2121, Tut21, Tvynr, Twister nt, Tyraios, Tyrol5, Tyw7, Ubuntu2, Ultimus, Uncle G, UnitedStatesian, Unixer, Unixxx, Urod, Uselesswarrior, Utcursch, UtherSRG, VX, Valerio81, VantagePoint, Vchimpanzee, VeLoCiTy89, Vera.tetrix, Viciodk, Viebel, Viento, Violetriga, Visor, Vizspring, Vocaro, Volt4ire, Vvidetta, WJBscribe, Wasimbargujar, Wayne Slam, Wbrameld, Wdyoung, Web-Crawling Stickler, Webmink, Weregerbil, Wesley crossman, Wgw2024, Wgw4, White Cat, Whosyourjudas, Wiggin15, Wik, WikiLeon, Wikianon, Wikipelli, Wikipendant, Wikiwerks, Wikiwikiwifi, Will Beback Auto, William Allen Simpson, William987, Wimt, Windchaser, Winterst, Wknight94, Wlievens, Wmahan, Wonko, Wootery, Wowus, Wrp103, Wsaryada, WurmWoode, Ww, Wyredchris, Wzwz, X deadly Snipez, Xan 213, Xaosflux, Xelgen, Xezbeth, Xinconnu, Xpodmaniac, Xproject, Yamaguchi先生, Yamamoto Ichiro, Yamla, Yozh, Yulracso, Yurik, Yurivict, ZacBowling, Zawersh, Zazpot, Zekeo, Zenohockey, Zijian, Zik-Zak, Zxcvbnm, Zyphrix, Ævar Arnfjörð Bjarmason, 六脉飞天牛, 2517 anonymous edits

Java Research License *Source*: http://en.wikipedia.org/w/index.php?oldid=387272346 *Contributors*: Austin Hair, FleetCommand, JVz, Slaporte, 3 anonymous edits

Java concurrency *Source*: http://en.wikipedia.org/w/index.php?oldid=394561851 *Contributors*: Abortz, Alvin-cs, Anwar saadat, Black Pepper, Chowbok, Ipsign, JonHarder, M4gnum0n, Mati22081979, Veinor, Vonfraginoff, 8 anonymous edits

JavaOne *Source*: http://en.wikipedia.org/w/index.php?oldid=387088571 *Contributors*: Alainr345, Andries, AnnaP, Eloquence, Felixschrape, Inonit, Jamelan, Jjaazz, Jpo, KJen1, Khym Chanur, Mahmoud farahat, Mhyiu0167, NapoliRoma, Neilc, Nnivi, Quatloo, Raysonho, RedWolf, Rjclaudio, Sohale, Stumps, Vsync, WOSlinker, 18 anonymous edits

K virtual machine *Source*: http://en.wikipedia.org/w/index.php?oldid=366541182 *Contributors*: Alainr345, Alex.ryazantsev, Cybercobra, Dicklyon, Frappucino, Interiot, Joel Saks, Nfwu, Phronima, SFC9394, Stux, Van helsing, 4 anonymous edits

OMS Video *Source*: http://en.wikipedia.org/w/index.php?oldid=364295160 *Contributors*: H3g3m0n, Jec, Kathleen.wright5, Rjwilmsi, Tinucherian, 6 anonymous edits

Oak (programming language) *Source*: http://en.wikipedia.org/w/index.php?oldid=392792323 *Contributors*: Csl77, Hervegirod, Hmains, Loadmaster, Ohconfucius, Paul Foxworthy, Rich Farmbrough, Ryan suchocki, 7 anonymous edits

Open Media Commons *Source*: http://en.wikipedia.org/w/index.php?oldid=334364555 *Contributors*: John Yesberg, Mike Linksvayer, Mipadi, That Guy, From That Show!

Open Source University Meetup *Source*: http://en.wikipedia.org/w/index.php?oldid=313271577 *Contributors*: Kopf1988, TimTay, 2 anonymous edits

Pixo *Source*: http://en.wikipedia.org/w/index.php?oldid=379827666 *Contributors*: A5b, Aboutime, AlexHOUSE, Allo002, BenFrantzDale, Cwbh, DisasterManX, Dmccarty, Dwightk, EdoDodo, Eptin, Evice, Gadavis, Gavin86, Gogo Dodo, Grstain, Jaraalbe, Jreferee, Libertyforall1776, Lode Runner, MSTCrow, Michael Grinberg, MigGroningen, Mxn, Nachmore, Nick Number, Nicolas1981, Pixoconcept, Psantora, RJFJR, Rubber cat, SD6-Agent, Stan Shebs, The Inedible Bulk, UkPaolo, 33 anonymous edits

Project DReaM *Source*: http://en.wikipedia.org/w/index.php?oldid=395813232 *Contributors*: CALR, CanisRufus, Deville, Dwarfpower, EGGS, Epolk, Frap, Mike Linksvayer, Mipadi, Pharos, R'n'B, Raysonho, Rjwilmsi, Tomjacobs-sun, 2 anonymous edits

Proximity communication *Source*: http://en.wikipedia.org/w/index.php?oldid=387913494 *Contributors*: A5b, GoingBatty, Raysonho, Warrior4321, 2 anonymous edits

SUN workstation *Source*: http://en.wikipedia.org/w/index.php?oldid=315200759 *Contributors*: Jpbowen, NapoliRoma, Robert.Harker, 1 anonymous edits

Jonathan I. Schwartz *Source*: http://en.wikipedia.org/w/index.php?oldid=397286345 *Contributors*: AaronSw, Ajping, Altenmann, Barek, Bearcat, CalJW, CarolGray, Chealer, Chochopk, Crewcut, D6, Doug Bell, Edcolins, EddieC Vito, Emperorkanishka, Ericjstudios, Frap, Fuhghettaboutit, Gazpacho, Geni, Happyxcao, Japanese Searobin, Jarchitect, JohnCD, Jsavit, Jvlentini, Kingka, Libertyforall1776, MMG Julien C, Mackensen, Meh130, MuthuKutty, N2e, NapoliRoma, NightMonkey, Norsktroll, Paul422, Pax:Vobiscum, Pen island101, Pmsyyz, Redjar, Rich Farmbrough, Rob.bastholm, RockMFR, SDC, Saint-Paddy, Schmiteye, Sillygates, Stevenmitchell, SunMicrosystems, T@nn, Tabletop, Techsharky, TimboNelson, Tmd, Toussaint, Useight, Vlad, Webmink, Wikieditoroftoday, Ysangkok, Yuriybrisk, 60 anonymous edits

Starfire video prototype *Source*: http://en.wikipedia.org/w/index.php?oldid=384787762 *Contributors*: Analoguedragon, Chris the speller, DXBari, Ddama, J 1982, Jpbowen, JustAGal, Mattl, Maury Markowitz, Midgley, Peter S., Reedy, Sassf, Stifle, TMC1221, Toghome, TubularWorld, Vlad, Wkreth, Yitscar, 3 anonymous edits

Storage Technology Corporation *Source*: http://en.wikipedia.org/w/index.php?oldid=387832625 *Contributors*: A D Monroe III, A Nobody, Alex.muller, Altenmann, Austinmurphy, Catapult, Chowbok, Cmr08, Edcolins, Ekilfoil, Feydey, GregorB, Ian Pitchford, Jt1969, Kadin2048, Kubanczyk, Melaen, Miremare, Ozrob, PKT, Pete212, Phliang, ShadowHntr, Stormrose, Swarm, TapeLady, TimTay, Twostardav, UnitedStatesian, Welsh, Zahman, Zubdub, 51 anonymous edits

StorageTek tape formats *Source*: http://en.wikipedia.org/w/index.php?oldid=398623632 *Contributors*: Austinmurphy, Bobblewik, Cscct, Kubanczyk, MBisanz, Thunderbird2, 15 anonymous edits

Sun Certified Professional *Source*: http://en.wikipedia.org/w/index.php?oldid=399350096 *Contributors*: (aeropagitica), A. B., Aaerrolla, Abelson, Ainze, Akgupta, Albinjoseph, Alvin-cs, AndrewHowse, BenSWiki, Bonadea, Caomhin, Centrx, Chiok, Chowbok, Chrissyboi, CommonsDelinker, D6, DARTH SIDIOUS 2, Danroa, Darklilac, Defixio, Doug Bell, Eighta, Ettrig, Gayam.ashwin.reddy, Gfluitt, Ghettoblaster, Gnashes30, Hanumantd, Imaseo, Imroy, Ishanthasiribaddana, JavaGuy, Jems420, Kirivarnan, Kkm010, Kks krishna, Kokonaing9, Krzyk2, LogicDictates, M.B, MER-C, MParaz, Mafutrct, Matt Crypto, Mjchonoles, MoistPup, Nakon, Nihlist, Nohara, Ohnoitsjamie, Omarbantaa, Partha1022, Quarl, Rich Farmbrough, Robert

Weemeyer, Ronz, Santoshb, Sceptre, Sciamachy, ScottW, Sheelpa, Shepard, Shoejar, Stratwine, TYelliot, TastyPoutine, TheJC, Themfromspace, Thiseye, Toussaint, Udittmer, Victorwss, WLU, Wmahan, Zombiflava, Zzuuzz, Микола Зайкін, 190 anonymous edits

Sun Cloud *Source*: http://en.wikipedia.org/w/index.php?oldid=354701805 *Contributors*: Altenmann, Armando82, Ash.banerjee@gmail.com, Bovineone, Centrx, DragonflySixtyseven, Gkrish, Inimino, JLaTondre, JPG-GR, Kkm010, Mipadi, Nakakapagpabagabag, NapoliRoma, PdDemeter, Raysonho, Rjwilmsi, SamJohnston, SteveLoughran, Thunderbird2, Toussaint, 12 anonymous edits

Sun Community Source License *Source*: http://en.wikipedia.org/w/index.php?oldid=354483733 *Contributors*: Slaporte

Sun Industry Standards Source License *Source*: http://en.wikipedia.org/w/index.php?oldid=366622605 *Contributors*: Afiler, CalJW, Closedmouth, Erik Sandberg, Frap, Gronky, Hansan, Joseph Dwayne, Milomedes, Minghong, Pearle, Pmsyyz, Raysonho, Rmky87, Rune.welsh, Superm401, Tokek, Woodjr, 13 anonymous edits

Sun Microsystems Laboratories *Source*: http://en.wikipedia.org/w/index.php?oldid=391655814 *Contributors*: Altenmann, Jpbowen, Raysonho, Tikiwont, Toussaint, 1 anonymous edits

Sun Web Developer Pack *Source*: http://en.wikipedia.org/w/index.php?oldid=398843142 *Contributors*: Alainr345, Ijevans, Jasdom1994, Rjwilmsi, Uncle Milty, 3 anonymous edits

Sun-1 *Source*: http://en.wikipedia.org/w/index.php?oldid=387339075 *Contributors*: Akradecki, Altenmann, Bovineone, Chris the speller, CommonsDelinker, Gardar Rurak, GioCM, Iridescent, Jdabney, Jpbowen, Letdorf, MarkusHagenlocher, Mmap, NapoliRoma, Qwertyus, Ramu50, Rees11, Rich Farmbrough, Rjwilmsi, Robert.Harker, Sun-collector, Surv1v4l1st, 6 anonymous edits

Write once, run anywhere *Source*: http://en.wikipedia.org/w/index.php?oldid=366363860 *Contributors*: Aavviof, Benc, Borisblue, Cfeet77, Chu Jetcheng, Cyrius, Easyas12c, Hervegirod, Jimktrains, Jondel, Jstupple7, Mnemo, Napi, NapoliRoma, Ninjagecko, Pontillo, RedWolf, SebastianBreier, Steve-o, Tdc6502, The Wild Falcon, Theda, Tregoweth, Wikipelli, 22 anonymous edits

Image Sources, Licenses and Contributors

Image:13W3_Stecker.jpg *Source*: http://en.wikipedia.org/w/index.php?title=File:13W3_Stecker.jpg *License*: Creative Commons Attribution-Sharealike 2.5 *Contributors*: User:Afrank99

Image:DB13W3_Pinout.svg *Source*: http://en.wikipedia.org/w/index.php?title=File:DB13W3_Pinout.svg *License*: Public Domain *Contributors*: Afrank99, Heron2, Mobius, Reactor

Image:DSubminiatures.svg *Source*: http://en.wikipedia.org/w/index.php?title=File:DSubminiatures.svg *License*: Public Domain *Contributors*: Mobius, Tothwolf, WikipediaMaster, 1 anonymous edits

Image:DB13W3 Diagram.svg *Source*: http://en.wikipedia.org/w/index.php?title=File:DB13W3_Diagram.svg *License*: Public Domain *Contributors*: Afrank99, Mobius, WikipediaMaster

Image:13W3 Stecker.jpg *Source*: http://en.wikipedia.org/w/index.php?title=File:13W3_Stecker.jpg *License*: Creative Commons Attribution-Sharealike 2.5 *Contributors*: User:Afrank99

Image:SVGA port.jpg *Source*: http://en.wikipedia.org/w/index.php?title=File:SVGA_port.jpg *License*: Public Domain *Contributors*: Duncan Lithgow

Image:Dsubs.png *Source*: http://en.wikipedia.org/w/index.php?title=File:Dsubs.png *License*: GNU Free Documentation License *Contributors*: user:Heron

Image:DD50 male pcb mounting d-sub connector close-up.jpg *Source*: http://en.wikipedia.org/w/index.php?title=File:DD50_male_pcb_mounting_d-sub_connector_close-up.jpg *License*: Public Domain *Contributors*: User:Mike1024

Image:9 pin d-sub connector male closeup.jpg *Source*: http://en.wikipedia.org/w/index.php?title=File:9_pin_d-sub_connector_male_closeup.jpg *License*: Public Domain *Contributors*: User:Mike1024

Image:DE9 Diagram.svg *Source*: http://en.wikipedia.org/w/index.php?title=File:DE9_Diagram.svg *License*: Public Domain *Contributors*: Mobius, WikipediaMaster

File:Sun Oracle logo.png *Source*: http://en.wikipedia.org/w/index.php?title=File:Sun_Oracle_logo.png *License*: unknown *Contributors*: Juux, Koman90, Reisio

File:Decrease2.svg *Source*: http://en.wikipedia.org/w/index.php?title=File:Decrease2.svg *License*: Public Domain *Contributors*: User:Sarang

File:Sun-1 Badge.jpg *Source*: http://en.wikipedia.org/w/index.php?title=File:Sun-1_Badge.jpg *License*: unknown *Contributors*: NapoliRoma

File:Sun Microsystems 1980s logo.gif *Source*: http://en.wikipedia.org/w/index.php?title=File:Sun_Microsystems_1980s_logo.gif *License*: unknown *Contributors*: NapoliRoma

Image:Sun Microsystems logo.svg *Source*: http://en.wikipedia.org/w/index.php?title=File:Sun_Microsystems_logo.svg *License*: unknown *Contributors*: Plastikspork, Tkgd2007, 1 anonymous edits

Image:Wfm sun agnews.jpg *Source*: http://en.wikipedia.org/w/index.php?title=File:Wfm_sun_agnews.jpg *License*: Public Domain *Contributors*: Arnux, EugeneZelenko, Finlay McWalter, NapoliRoma, Sandivas

Image:Sunagnewscampusbldgs2122.jpg *Source*: http://en.wikipedia.org/w/index.php?title=File:Sunagnewscampusbldgs2122.jpg *License*: Creative Commons Attribution-Sharealike 3.0 *Contributors*: Coolcaesar

Image:SunCanada.jpg *Source*: http://en.wikipedia.org/w/index.php?title=File:SunCanada.jpg *License*: Public Domain *Contributors*: User:Raysonho

Image:SunRackMountServers.jpg *Source*: http://en.wikipedia.org/w/index.php?title=File:SunRackMountServers.jpg *License*: Public Domain *Contributors*: User:Raysonho

Image:SPARCstation 1.jpg *Source*: http://en.wikipedia.org/w/index.php?title=File:SPARCstation_1.jpg *License*: Public Domain *Contributors*: Original uploader was Fourdee at en.wikipedia

Image:VirtualBox2.png *Source*: http://en.wikipedia.org/w/index.php?title=File:VirtualBox2.png *License*: Trademarked *Contributors*: User:Hidro

Image:Bellingleeconnector.jpg *Source*: http://en.wikipedia.org/w/index.php?title=File:Bellingleeconnector.jpg *License*: Creative Commons Attribution 3.0 *Contributors*: Original uploader was Abisys at it.wikipedia

Image:BNC connector.jpg *Source*: http://en.wikipedia.org/w/index.php?title=File:BNC_connector.jpg *License*: GNU Free Documentation License *Contributors*: User Meggar on en.wikipedia

Image:PICT7389 trimmed-C.jpg *Source*: http://en.wikipedia.org/w/index.php?title=File:PICT7389_trimmed-C.jpg *License*: GNU Free Documentation License *Contributors*: Original uploader was Jmb at en.wikipedia

Image:F Connector.jpg *Source*: http://en.wikipedia.org/w/index.php?title=File:F_Connector.jpg *License*: Public Domain *Contributors*: Original uploader was Andux at en.wikipedia

Image:N-Connector.jpg *Source*: http://en.wikipedia.org/w/index.php?title=File:N-Connector.jpg *License*: Creative Commons Attribution-Sharealike 2.0 *Contributors*: User:Fallschirmjäger, User:Schwindp

Image:TNC with BNC.jpg *Source*: http://en.wikipedia.org/w/index.php?title=File:TNC_with_BNC.jpg *License*: GNU Free Documentation License *Contributors*: Bongoman, 1 anonymous edits

Image:Twinlead.gif *Source*: http://en.wikipedia.org/w/index.php?title=File:Twinlead.gif *License*: Creative Commons Attribution 3.0 *Contributors*: User:LuckyLouie

Image:UHF-Connector.png *Source*: http://en.wikipedia.org/w/index.php?title=File:UHF-Connector.png *License*: Creative Commons Attribution-Sharealike 2.0 *Contributors*: User:schwindp

Image:Vga-cable.jpg *Source*: http://en.wikipedia.org/w/index.php?title=File:Vga-cable.jpg *License*: Public Domain *Contributors*: User:Evan-Amos

Image:Dvi-cable.jpg *Source*: http://en.wikipedia.org/w/index.php?title=File:Dvi-cable.jpg *License*: Public Domain *Contributors*: User:Evan-Amos

Image:DVI-D Connector.jpg *Source*: http://en.wikipedia.org/w/index.php?title=File:DVI-D_Connector.jpg *License*: Creative Commons Attribution-Sharealike 2.5 *Contributors*: 32bitmaschine, Keeleysam, Sergei, Sven

Image:Kobushi-mini-dvi.jpg *Source*: http://en.wikipedia.org/w/index.php?title=File:Kobushi-mini-dvi.jpg *License*: Creative Commons Attribution 2.5 *Contributors*: User Joeyhagedorn on en.wikipedia

Image:Apple-MacBook-Air-Ports.jpg *Source*: http://en.wikipedia.org/w/index.php?title=File:Apple-MacBook-Air-Ports.jpg *License*: Creative Commons Attribution-Sharealike 2.0 *Contributors*: User:LSDSL

File:DMS-59.jpg *Source*: http://en.wikipedia.org/w/index.php?title=File:DMS-59.jpg *License*: Public Domain *Contributors*: GreyCat, Nyttend, Search255

Image:AppleDisplayConnector.jpg *Source*: http://en.wikipedia.org/w/index.php?title=File:AppleDisplayConnector.jpg *License*: Creative Commons Attribution-Sharealike 2.5 *Contributors*: User:Ali@gwc.org.uk

Image:HDMI connector-male 2 sharp Δ0059.jpg *Source*: http://en.wikipedia.org/w/index.php?title=File:HDMI_connector-male_2_sharp_Δ0059.jpg *License*: unknown *Contributors*: D-Kuru, Tony Wills

Image:SVideoConnector.jpg *Source*: http://en.wikipedia.org/w/index.php?title=File:SVideoConnector.jpg *License*: Public Domain *Contributors*: 32bitmaschine, Clemente, Fabartus, Mobius, 1 anonymous edits

Image:MiniDIN-8 Diagram.svg *Source*: http://en.wikipedia.org/w/index.php?title=File:MiniDIN-8_Diagram.svg *License*: Public Domain *Contributors*: Mobius, WikipediaMaster

Image:MiniDIN-9 Diagram.svg *Source*: http://en.wikipedia.org/w/index.php?title=File:MiniDIN-9_Diagram.svg *License*: Public Domain *Contributors*: Mobius, WikipediaMaster, 1 anonymous edits

Image:Pseudo miniDIN-7 Diagram.png *Source*: http://en.wikipedia.org/w/index.php?title=File:Pseudo_miniDIN-7_Diagram.png *License*: Public Domain *Contributors*: user:andrewa

Image:Pseudo miniDIN-8 Diagram.png *Source*: http://en.wikipedia.org/w/index.php?title=File:Pseudo_miniDIN-8_Diagram.png *License*: Public Domain *Contributors*: Original uploader was Radical Mallard at en.wikipedia

Image:Pseudo miniDIN-8b Diagram.png *Source*: http://en.wikipedia.org/w/index.php?title=File:Pseudo_miniDIN-8b_Diagram.png *License*: Public Domain *Contributors*: User:Radical Mallard

Image:Pseudo miniDIN-9 Diagram.png *Source*: http://en.wikipedia.org/w/index.php?title=File:Pseudo_miniDIN-9_Diagram.png *License*: Public Domain *Contributors*: user:andrewa

Image:Pseudo miniDIN-9b Diagram.png *Source*: http://en.wikipedia.org/w/index.php?title=File:Pseudo_miniDIN-9b_Diagram.png *License*: Public Domain *Contributors*: Radical Mallard, 1 anonymous edits

Image:Pseudo miniDIN-10 Diagram.png *Source*: http://en.wikipedia.org/w/index.php?title=File:Pseudo_miniDIN-10_Diagram.png *License*: Public Domain *Contributors*: User:Radical Mallard

Image:Pseudo miniDIN-10b Diagram.png *Source*: http://en.wikipedia.org/w/index.php?title=File:Pseudo_miniDIN-10b_Diagram.png *License*: Public Domain *Contributors*: User:Radical Mallard

Image:Composite-cables.jpg *Source*: http://en.wikipedia.org/w/index.php?title=File:Composite-cables.jpg *License*: Public Domain *Contributors*: User:Evan-Amos

Image:SCART 20050724 002.jpg *Source*: http://en.wikipedia.org/w/index.php?title=File:SCART_20050724_002.jpg *License*: Public Domain *Contributors*: User:bergsten

Image:D4 video connector.jpg *Source*: http://en.wikipedia.org/w/index.php?title=File:D4_video_connector.jpg *License*: Public Domain *Contributors*: Max Smith

Image:Mini-VGA.jpg *Source*: http://en.wikipedia.org/w/index.php?title=File:Mini-VGA.jpg *License*: Public Domain *Contributors*: GreyCat, Jgremillot, TommyBee, WikipediaMaster

License